# The Price Guide to
# METAL TOYS

Gordon Gardiner and Alistair Morris

Antique Collectors' Club

ISBN 0 902028 92 8

Reprinted 1982

CIP DATA
Gardiner, Gordon
 The Price Guide to Metal Toys.
 1. Toys — Collectors and collecting
 2. Toys
 I. Title   II. Morris, Alistair
 III. Antique Collectors' Club
 688.7'2'075    TS2301.T7


Published for the Antique Collectors' Club
by the Antique Collectors' Club Ltd.



Printed in England by
Baron Publishing, Woodbridge, Suffolk

*The end papers show a selection of detachable toy keys, c.1920-50. The Hornby key, centre right, had a dual use: for testing gauge of rails as well as winding. The Schuco starting handle key is bottom right.*

# Contents

(Motifs: The motifs beside the subject sections above are repeated at the top of each page of the relevant section.)

# Price Revision List

Published annually in December

The usefulness of a book containing prices rapidly diminishes as market values change.

In order to keep the prices in this book updated, a price revision list will be issued in December each year. This will record the major price changes in the values of the items covered under the various headings in the book.

To ensure you receive the price revision list, complete the pro forma invoice inserted in this book and send it to the address below:

**ANTIQUE COLLECTORS' CLUB
5 CHURCH STREET, WOODBRIDGE, SUFFOLK, ENGLAND**

# Colour Plates

# Acknowledgements

The authors wish to express their thanks to:

| | |
|---|---|
| Jenni Clarke | Hilary Kay |
| F.L. Mountford | A.G. Blackstone |
| Bob Dawes | Hazel Gardiner |
| Peter Moore | Cherry Lewis |

W. Leslie Weller, F.R.I.C.S., F.S.V.A.

In addition our thanks to the following for their kind permission to reproduce illustrations from original catalogues:

Messrs. Bassett-Lowke, Britain Ltd., Morris Vulcan Ltd., Meccano Ltd.

# Photographic Credits

| | |
|---|---|
| Sotheby King and Chasemore | Sotheby's Belgravia |
| Sotheby Bearne | Sotheby Parke Bernet N.Y. |
| Motor Book Postal Auctions | Dawes & Billings |
| A. Weller, Esq. | R. Griffiths, Esq. |

and to others who have given permission to photograph items from private collections.

# Foreword

Quite recently in a select toy sale in New York, an attractive Marklin battleship sold for the surely record auction price of $21,000. This must have caused surprise to a number of people who are used to seeing such prices relating to fine furniture or paintings.

Considering a child's carefree attitude to toys, it is pleasing to find that many have survived and are appreciated by a growing number of collectors.

I trust that the reader, whether he be a specialist, generalist or bystander, will find this book a useful contribution to his reference library.

W. Leslie Weller

# Introduction

In the last decade the collecting of toys has become accepted as an interesting and rewarding subject. One can marvel not only at the ingenuity of an early novelty toy, but also at the visual attractiveness of certain cars, trams, etc. Indeed the whole history of 20th century transport can be encompassed in miniature by the toy. Many vehicle enthusiasts no doubt have a few toy models, as an extension of their interest. The market for toys is now a truly international one, with leading auctioneers holding regular toy sales, a fact which has no doubt saved many toys from obscurity due to the pre- and post-sale publicity. There are now a number of specialist toy dealers, many of whom have shops, and the auto jumble or collectors market are also good hunting grounds.

As with all forms of investment, it is better to form a collection which pleases rather than attempt to acquire an accumulation of unrelated, poor condition toys. Whereas most toys have proved to be a good investment, condition would appear to have been a prime factor, as it is in many other forms of collecting.

There have recently appeared on the market several fine books on toys and toy collecting, but these invariably illustrate only the fine and rare examples which the average collector cannot envisage owning. This book, with a few exceptions, covers items which have appeared on the market within the last few years and which will be within the reach of the new collector. We make no apologies for illustrating damaged examples, as these now have a place in collecting — indeed specialist toy restorers now exist. The book covers a period of approximately seventy years, which included the mass-production period of toys made basically in metal. Games and soft toys have not been included.

This book is intended as a visual reference, with some general-interest comments, and as a price guide. It is intended for use by collector and dealer alike and much trouble has been taken to ensure that photographs illustrate the prime points. In some instances more than one view has been used to emphasise a point and colour illustrations have been incorporated to bring back to life the aesthetic charm of toys.

The authors are aware that when assessing values of toys (as indeed many other types of antiques and collectable items) there may be considerable variations from area to area, and that both auction and dealer prices are also subject to many fluctuating conditions. In researching prices for this book we have endeavoured to take these into account and from necessity an average price has had to be assessed; where toys are exceedingly rare the market value can make vast strides, but also, due to the increasing popularity of toy collecting, some common items may become overrated by the beginner. Careful attention must be given to grading — remember toys were made to be played with — and mint examples are therefore scarce. Collectors are encouraged to visit some of the very good toy museums which now exist in their own right, while the study of old auction catalogues with illustrations are also useful guides.

It will be noticed that in the introduction to most sections use is made, under the heading 'Value Points', of from three or four + marks. They are intended to convey the monetary importance of the special design features. The existence of + + + + would lift the piece over the top of the price bracket shown. + + + would put it towards the top of the price bracket.

*Colour Plate 1. A scarce Carette gauge II, live steam 2-2-0 locomotive and tender having track and cab-operated reversing mechanism, double-acting steam cylinders with exhaust into funnel, whistle, safety valve, dome and starting tap. Also two Carette carriages and a guard's van. Circa 1903. 41 cm long. Many of these early steam locomotives work well today, but their pulling power is invariably diminished. (See also 16, page 21.)*

*Colour Plate 2. A superb example of a gauge III, 4-2-0 live steam locomotive and tender by Georges Carette. Note the cab side numbers: III = gauge III, 67 = 67mm gauge width. First decade 20th century. 57.8 cm long.*

*£1,300 — £1,600*

# Trains

## Early Models

From the 1840s the idea of toy trains became a reality. Early models did not have rails, were of wood or metal construction and either of a 'pull-along' or simple steam type. Towards the end of the century clockwork mechanisms were introduced and electricity was tried and tested. From the 1860s the German manufacturers began to dominate the market, overtaking American production, and this position held until after the First World War.

Just as in real life gauges were standardised enabling interchangeability of products, although occasionally modifications to couplings had to be made. At the turn of the century gauges I-IV were available and a useful quick guide to gauge identification can be found on some locomotives and coaches in the form of a lithographed Roman numeral above Arabic numbers: $\frac{II}{54}$ is therefore gauge II 54 mm. A few years later 0 gauge became generally available and this, being space saving, enabled more complex layouts to be designed. It is interesting to note that gauge I is the same scale as the majority of Britains products.

Most locomotives from this period will be clockwork, with steam a close second. Early examples are hand enamelled, the later ones being lithographed.

With regard to condition, completeness of detail especially with the slightly later models is of prime importance. With steam models one has to accept deteriorated paintwork on and adjacent to the boiler unless the model has never been steamed (very rare).

Mint paintwork to steam models probably indicates restoration. This is acceptable if well executed and indeed, since some models came as kits, the quality of assembly and finish varies considerably.

Where required, correct tenders affect value considerably. If a loco is purchased separately, bear in mind that some years may pass before a suitable replacement tender is found. When purchased separately, tenders may appear to have unrealistically high prices.

Certain locomotives from this period had a two-speed mechanism with reverse so that braking and reversing could be controlled from the track.

Although most locomotives are of German origin, the liveries produced for this country will be of British regions. The German home market product is distinctive in its attempts at streamlining, for example a pointed smokebox door and cab.

*Value Point*
Presence of original box + + + +

## Later Models

From the toy angle, steam propulsion was nearing the end of its life. In the 1920s gauge 0 was firmly established; under the title of 'Table Top Railway' 00 gauge was introduced in 1923-24. These scales reached a far wider market due to their size and price and by 1938 Hornby had announced their famous 'Dublo' range. The name Hornby is prominent in this period. Its founder, Frank Hornby, was already famous through his invention of Meccano and the trains appearing in 1924 were of nut and bolt construction, a direct development of that idea.

Inspection of wheels and other cast parts on British produced models is recommended, since during the 1930s reduction of lead content in the alloy produced metal fatigue which in turn led to a cracking or crumbling of these parts. Post-war this problem is seldom encountered.

A wide range of quality is now available and models vary from quite accurate scale type to others of crude simplicity. Remember that not all models from this period need be valuable.

The present popularity of 00 gauge, and particularly 'Dublo', can be attributed to the quality and comprehensiveness of the range, and today's enthusiast no doubt makes an important contribution to the market value of second-hand 00 gauge items. It is interesting to note that although the majority of these 00 gauge items are electric some were also produced in clockwork.

*Value Point*
Presence of box, instructions, guarantee + + +

## PARTICULARS OF RAILS.

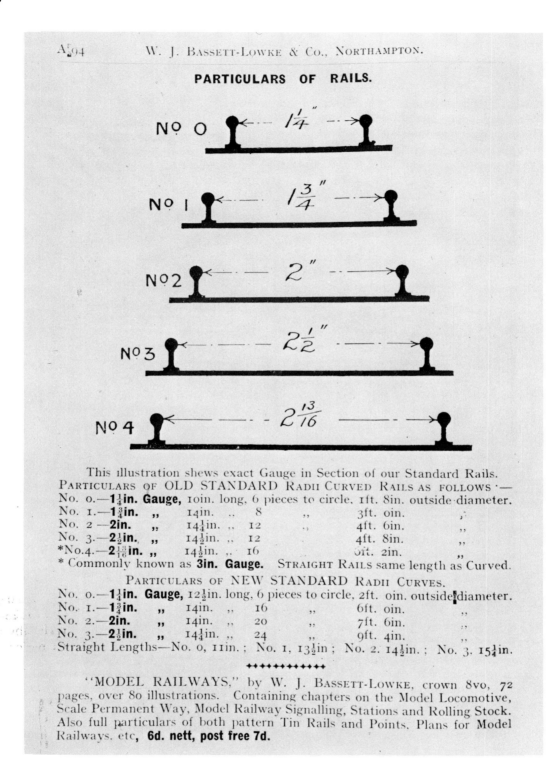

This illustration shews exact Gauge in Section of our Standard Rails.

PARTICULARS OF OLD STANDARD RADII CURVED RAILS AS FOLLOWS :—

No. 0.—**1¼in. Gauge,** 10in. long, 6 pieces to circle, 1ft. 8in. outside diameter.
No. 1.—**1¾in.** ,,   14in. ,,   8    ,,     3ft. 0in.     ,,
No. 2.—**2in.** ,,   14¼in. ,,   12   ,,     4ft. 6in.     ,,
No. 3.—**2½in.** ,,   14¼in. ,,   12   ,,     4ft. 8in.     ,,
*No. 4.—**2¹³⁄₁₆in.** ,,   14½in. ,,   16   ,,     5ft. 2in.     ,,

\* Commonly known as **3in. Gauge.** STRAIGHT RAILS same length as Curved.

PARTICULARS OF NEW STANDARD RADII CURVES.

No. 0.—**1¼in. Gauge,** 12½in. long, 6 pieces to circle, 2ft. 0in. outside diameter.
No. 1.—**1¾in.** ,,   14in. ,,   16   ,,     6ft. 0in.     ,,
No. 2.—**2in.** ,,   14in. ,,   20   ,,     7ft. 6in.     ,,
No. 3.—**2½in.** ,,   14¼in. ,,   24   ,,     9ft. 4in.     ,,

Straight Lengths—No. 0, 11in. ; No. 1, 13½in ; No. 2. 14½in. ; No. 3. 15¼in.

+++++++++++

"MODEL RAILWAYS," by W. J. BASSETT-LOWKE, crown 8vo, 72 pages, over 80 illustrations. Containing chapters on the Model Locomotive, Scale Permanent Way, Model Railway Signalling, Stations and Rolling Stock. Also full particulars of both pattern Tin Rails and Points. Plans for Model Railways, etc, **6d. nett, post free 7d.**

This 'Particulars of Rails' reproduced from Bassett Lowke's catalogue 1905-6 provides easy identification when measuring wheel flanges on locos and rolling stock.

1 A group of early live steam locomotives often referred to as piddlers or dribblers. Note the variations on positions of cylinders, etc. Manufactured in the mid- to late 19th century. Sizes vary from 15 cm to 23.5 cm. Some models were available in kit form for home assembly.

| | | |
|---|---|---|
| *Clockwise* | *12 noon* | *£70 — £100* |
| | *1* | *£70 — £100* |
| | *3* | *£80 — £120* |
| | *5* | *£60 — £100* |
| | *7* | *£80 — £100* |
| | *9* | *£120 — £140 (note elegant wheels and fine detail)* |
| | *11* | *£60 — £100* |

2 A rare 19th century French tinplate carpet toy train comprising locomotive, tender and three carriages. Circa 1870. 38 cm overall. Interesting but underrated at the time of writing.

*£80 — £120*

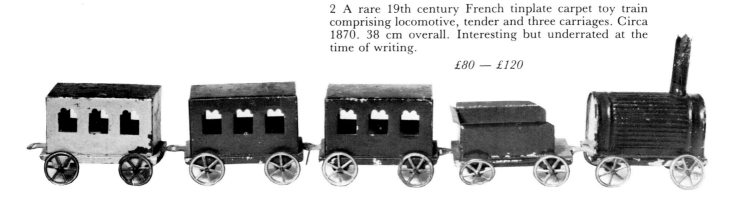

3 Another rare early tinplate carpet toy train, this example by Faivre, is 48 cm overall and comprises a locomotive, tender bearing 'No. 15', 1st and 2nd class carriages and guard's wagon. Circa 1880. It is better proportioned and more attractive than the previous item.

*£225 — £300*

4 Two late Victorian cast-iron train sets both made by Wallworks, Manchester. Typical examples of English semi-scale models using a traditional metal.

*£80 — £100 (top)*
*£80 — £120 (bottom)*

5 An interesting early 3in. gauge dribbler or piddler 2-2-2 locomotive, constructed almost entirely of brass, spirit fired, oscillating cylinders. Circa 1880. 23 cm long. Funnel missing.

*£120 — £160*

6 This gauge III 4-2-2 locomotive and tender is mainly of brass construction. The spirit fired boiler retaining evidence of paint. Cylinders, pierced splasher boxes, etc., complete with mahogany buffer beams. This is an early example dating from the last quarter of the 19th century. 57.8 cm long. These models are scarce but fall short of the main collector category, often being of unknown manufacture. Centre wheels missing from tender.

*£400 — £500*

7 An early 3½ in. gauge coal-fired live steam 4-4-0 locomotive and tender built by Darby and Co., Engineers, Newcastle on Tyne, 1888. This has a copper boiler and firebox and retains traces of livery. Models of this type are scarce and were produced in small numbers as they were not a commercial proposition; this makes them less attractive to the train collector.

*£180 — £220*

8 This quaint locomotive is an early example, c.1896, from the factory of Ernst Plank. The gauge III spirit fired locomotive comes complete with its tender bearing 'No. 500'. Locomotives of this period frequently carried name plates — this one 'Vulkan'. 36.2 cm overall.

*£200 — £250*

9 A scarce late 19th century Marklin gauge I live steam 0-4-0 locomotive. This model was fired by blow lamp arrangements through the cab and has external cylinders driving central crank-shaft and geared transmission to the iron wheels. The loco illustrated lacks tender and some fittings.

*£300 — £400*

10 A typical turn of the century Marklin 0-4-0 clockwork locomotive and tender in gauge II. Note the crude tender, external brake activating rod and shoe and high chimney. 33 cm overall.

*£400 — £500*

11 This early gauge IV live steam 0-4-0 locomotive together with its tender bears a resemblance to those built by Ernst Plank. These models are crude, and 'made up' copies are not unknown. 43.2 cm overall.

*£200 — £300*

12 A turn of the century Marklin gauge I 0-4-0 locomotive shown here together with its tender and two early Marklin four-wheeled 1st and 2nd class coaches. These models were hand enamelled and are known to be noisy in operation. Loco and tender 36.2 cm overall.

*£450 — £550*

13 A 3½ in. gauge model of a 2-4-0 locomotive, possibly a non-commercial product. It is live steam, painted green with red and black bands. Late 19th century. 48 cm long. The lack of a tender reduces the value considerably, possibly by as much as a third.

*£170 — £200*

14 Note the Marklin sectionalised foot-bridge with attractively pierced tin railings to simulate cast-iron work. Circa 1895-1900. Shown in the next illustration with a Marklin 0-4-0 gauge I clockwork locomotive.

*£40 — £80 (footbridge)*

15 Mechanically interesting due to its two speed clockwork forward and reverse mechanism, this early Marklin 0-4-0 gauge I locomotive also displays unusual non voided driving wheels for increased traction. External brake wheel rim operating, hand painted and lined. The rear wheels play no part in driving the locomotive and are free to rotate. Circa 1895-1900. It is finished in dark green livery with red, yellow and gold lining.

*£450 — £600*

16 This example of an uncommon gauge II live steam 2-2-0 locomotive was made by Carette, c.1902-3 and is typical of the type sold by Bassett-Lowke (see page 50 of Bassett-Lowke commemorative catalogue for similar locomotive). Shown here together with tender, Continental carriages and guard's van. (See also Colour Plate 1, page 14.)

*£450 — £600*

17 An example from Bing's extensive range of live steam locomotives, this fine spirit fired gauge I, 4-4-0 model of c.1904 has a six-wheeled tender. Bearing 'L.S.W.R.' livery, it still retains the original finish.

*£1,000 — £1,200*

18 From the gauge III range comes this superb Bing spirit fired live steam L.S.W.R. 4-4-0 locomotive and tender. The connecting rods are attractively fluted, while the mid-body section has perforated steel skirts, headlamps missing. Manufactured 1905. 63.5 cm overall.

*£1,500 — £2,000 (rare in original finish)*

19 Although incomplete, this scarce Carette 0-4-0 gauge II locomotive of c.1905 still holds collectors' interest due to its age. One wheel is missing and it should be remembered that parts are somewhat difficult to obtain for these scarcer gauges.

*£30 — £50 (in condition shown)*
*£150 — £200 (in sound condition with original four-wheeled tender)*

20  This Carette gauge I live steam spirit fired 2-2-0 locomotive complete with its tender has safety valve and whistle and was made about 1905. 39.5 cm long. Steam models which have been 'enjoyed' extensively invariably suffer paint loss from boiler and surrounding parts.

*£200 — £275*

21 Finished in Midland maroon livery, this Bing gauge I clockwork 0-4-0 locomotive No. 116 has rim operated brakes and was manufactured c.1905. Together with its four-wheeled tender, this livery is particularly attractive. 33.6 cm overall.

*£200 — £250*

22  A Bing gauge I  0-4-0 clockwork locomotive finished in 'LSWR' green livery complete with tender. Circa 1906. 35.5 cm overall.

*£200 — £250*

23  A scarce early Marklin gauge I clockwork 2-2-0 locomotive and tender (coupled wrongly), finished in original dark green gilt lined livery. Shown with Marklin 1st class passenger carriage painted dark blue, 2nd class passenger carriage painted red and a 'pakenwagen'. These sets invariably came as shown. Late 19th century.

*£400 — £500*

24 Complete with its attractively labelled box, a gauge 0 clockwork train set by Issmayer, comprising early style 0-2-2 locomotive tender and passenger carriages. Although a 'toy' and sold cheaply, the item is finely lithographed. Note the unnecessary damage to the upper right hand corner of the box caused by removal of dealer's or auction room label.

*£100 — £150*

25 Dating from c.1905, this rare and desirable 2½ in. gauge 4-4-0 spirit fired live steam locomotive and tender by Georges Carette retains much of its original olive green 'North Eastern' livery. Nicely appointed with hand rails, lubricators, headlamps, etc.

*£1,500 — £2,000*

26 By Ernst Plank, this 2-2-0 gauge I clockwork locomotive and tender bears the name 'Union' and has its original Midland Railway tender in chocolate brown livery. It is shown here together with a 'GNR' luggage and guard's van, probably by another maker (Carette).

*£100 — £150 (loco and tender)*
*£20 — £30 (luggage/guard's van)*

27 Possibly by Bing or Carette, this 2½ in. gauge 4-4-0 spirit fired live steam locomotive and tender illustrates as found condition displaying chips, scorches, etc. The model retains original headlamps, lubricators, etc. Black livery lined in red and yellow. Circa 1910.

*£700 — £1,000*

28 An offside view of the same locomotive again indicating as found condition; outside rod operated forward/reverse mechanism. Note the absence of connecting rods as intended.

29 Again in 'playworn' condition, a Bing 4-4-0, 2½ in. gauge live steam locomotive together with its 'LSWR' tender. Circa 1910. Note the Bing semaphore signal with working lamp.

*£500 — £700 (loco and tender)*
*£12 — £18 (signal)*

30 A Carette gauge I spirit fired live steam 2-2-0 locomotive and tender. Circa 1910. Black livery lined red and white. Note maker's trade marks on cab side and tender. Simple reciprocating action.

*£300 — £350*

31 Early for gauge 0, this GNR 0-4-0 clockwork locomotive and tender by Bing was sold with three four-wheeled 'G.N.R.' passenger carriages. Circa 1905. Also shown is a contemporary Bing petrol tanker.

*£150 — £180 (loco, tender, carriages)*
*£15 — £20 (petrol tanker)*

32 A scarce gauge 0 Carette 4-4-0 clockwork locomotive and non matching tender '375' finished in 'L & NWR' livery. This model has reversing mechanism. Some damage to buffers, couplings, etc., one headlamp missing. 33 cm overall.

*£120 — £140 (as shown)*
*£150 — £180 (in undamaged condition with original tender)*

33 A Carette gauge 0 spirit fired live steam 2-2-0 locomotive, tender, two coaches and guard's van. 'GNR' livery. Circa 1910. 76 cm long overall.

*£450 — £650 (as shown)*
*£25 — £40 (each, for coaches and van in sound condition)*

34 A scarce gauge II Bing clockwork 4-4-0 locomotive. This model has two-speed clockwork mechanism with brakes operating direct on to wheels. Headlamps missing. Circa 1912. Note embossed 'GBN' Bing trade mark to the front of boiler. (See also Colour Plate 3, page 31.)

*£150 — £180 (as shown)*
*£225 — £275 (with matching six-wheeled tender)*

35 Difficult to find in gauge I, this Bing spirit fired 4-4-0 locomotive 593 has attractive brass fittings and comes complete with its original tender, refinished overall. 57 cm long. Although well refinished, the model would be worth half as much again if totally original.

*£800 — £900*

36 A fine gauge III 0-4-0 clockwork locomotive by Bing, note headlamp missing which would have been mounted just in front of chimney. Finished in partly restored 'L.N.W.R.' black livery. Plate and name plate bear '7093' and 'King Edward'. Complete with six-wheeled tender. Circa 1910. 59 cm overall. The high price of this model is largely because of its scarcity in gauge III. Also shown a rake of two gauge III Bing passenger bogie coaches finished in 'L&NWR' livery with hinged roofs, open doors, etc., partially fitted interiors, partly repainted. 43.2 cm long. The high price is again due to scarcity of gauge.

*£1,000 — £1,200 (loco and tender)*
*£1,000 — £1,200 (pair of coaches)*

38 A 'Germanic' style gauge I live steam 4-4-0 locomotive by Bing, in black livery with red and gold lining. Circa 1912. 36 cm long. It lacks the tender, which should have eight wheels.

*£200 — £300*

37 Again the Germanic style is apparent in this Karl Bub gauge I clockwork locomotive complete with tender. Note '1-48' to cab, also the pointed cab roof. Dark green livery. Two Bub passenger carriages with opening doors. Circa 1912.

*£130 — £180 (as shown)*

39 By Georges Carette, this gauge I example of an 0-4-0 clockwork locomotive displays evidence of restoration, note replacement turned brass buffers, connecting rods, new cab roof, footplate, etc. Produced c.1914. Many pre-World War I locomotives will be found to have some restoration which is acceptable subject to price.

*£130 — £180 (as shown)*

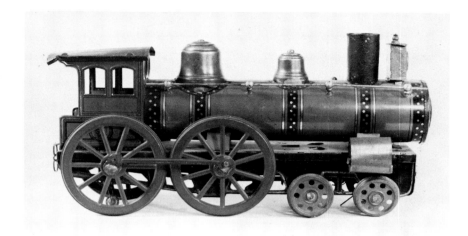

40 This novelty train by Günthermann operates without the benefit of rails, having clockwork mechanism driving the four coupled wheels and ringing a concealed bell at regular intervals. Such models are described as 'carpet' toys. 34 cm long.

*£50 — £80*

41 Extremely fine, this gauge II clockwork Bassett-Lowke 4-6-0 locomotive '1914 Patriot' and tender are finished in black livery with red and cream lining. It commemorates the fallen L&NWR employees in World War I. 71 cm overall, it is mounted on a length of display track.

*£700 — £1,000*

42 Although shabby, this gauge I spirit fired live steam Bing 4-4-0 locomotive is still desirable. Note the slightly domed smoke box door which is normally pointed, bogie missing, much paint chipping and some dents. Circa 1912. (See no. 38 for similar example.)

*£350 — £500*

43 Of unusual appearance, this 4-6-2 spirit fired live steam gauge I locomotive 'The Great Bear' was manufactured by Marklin and retailed through Gamages. Finished in scorched 'LNER' green livery. Eight-wheeled bogie tender. Circa 1912. 73.5 cm overall. One of the authors remembers parting with a 'Great Bear' chassis for £30! Rare.

*This model was sold at auction in 1978 for £2,500*

44 A fine gauge II 4-4-2 clockwork Atlantic locomotive and tender. Note a similar electric version of this model was available from Bassett-Lowke in 1911 at a cost of £30. (See also Colour Plate 4, page 31.)

*£300 — £500*

45 This 'Jupiter' clockwork gauge I 4-4-0 locomotive and tender by Bing in original 'L.N.W.R.' black livery shows a good complete example of a pre-World War I model. 51.5 cm.

*£500 — £700*
*(in 1979 the model, complete with original wooden box,*
*fetched £850)*

46 This example was available from A.W. Gamage and bears their retail mark. A gauge 0 clockwork 4-4-0 locomotive with its six-wheeled tender in 'GNR' green livery. 38 cm overall.

*£100 — £125*

47 A gauge I live steam spirit fired 0-4-0 locomotive and tender by Bing having double acting cylinders and smoke box regulator finished in 'G.N.R.' green livery paintwork distressed in boiler area.

*£225 — £300*

48 An inexpensive gauge 0 Carette clockwork locomotive, tender and passenger carriage. This example of a lightweight tinplate set is of simple construction and of a type manufactured c.1914-18.

*£40 — £60 (as shown)*

49 Again from the First World War period, a Bing gauge I clockwork 0-4-0 locomotive bearing 'GNR' livery, together with its four-wheeled tender. 35.5 cm.

*£180 — £225*

50 A Marklin gauge 0 electric 4-4-0 locomotive, E66/12920, having electric headlamps and a six-wheeled tender with rivet detail. Note the original paintwork has crazed badly. 40 cm overall.

*£300 (as shown)*
*£350 (with uncrazed paintwork)*

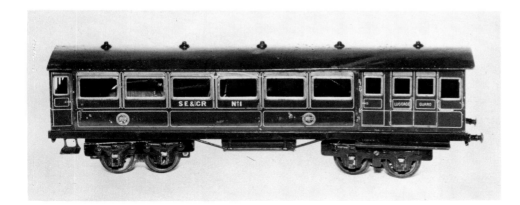

51 A scarce gauge I Carette eight-wheeled electric rail motor, the engine compartment enclosing an early electric motor which drives leading bogie, passenger section having fitted tinplate seats with guard's compartment at rear. This example retains a reasonable original finish in chocolate 'SE&CR' livery with yellow lining. 42 cm overall.

*£1,200 — £1,500*

*Colour Plate 3. With its 'GBN' trade mark embossed to the smoke box door, this gauge II clockwork 4-4-0 locomotive is the work of Bing, Nuremburg. Circa 1912. (See also 34, page 26.)*

*Colour Plate 4. An interesting 4-4-2, gauge II Atlantic clockwork locomotive, together with its six-wheeled tender with cast axle boxes. Although many similar examples were produced in Germany (by Bing and others) for Bassett-Lowke, collectors should satisfy themselves of the provenance of items since fine home made models do exist combining commercially made mechanisms. The example shown, though outwardly showing slight damage, is an interesting paradox of good commercial parts and doubtful workmanship, though this may be the result of fairly extensive repair and poor repainting. Circa 1912. 69 cm overall. (See also 44, page 29.)*

*Colour Plate 5.*

*Far right: A fine Hornby LMS compound locomotive, gauge 0 and having 20 volt electric mechanism, complete with its tender; wheels fatigued.*

*£100 — £150*

*Right: A fine example of Hornby's scarce gauge 0 Eton electric 4-4-0 locomotive and tender, the wheels on the model shown suffering from metal fatigue, otherwise very desirable. (See also 82, page 40.)*

52 This slightly retouched Bing gauge I 0-4-0 spirit fired live steam locomotive looks as though it requires more wheels, although this is its intended form. Black livery and complete with its 'L.N.W.R.' tender, it is later than the number on the side would indicate. 47 cm overall.

*£300 — £400*

53 A gauge 0 Karl Bub electric model railway comprising an 0-4-0 locomotive with a Bing four-wheeled tender and a four-wheeled guard's van.

*£70 — £90 (loco only)*

54 Probably Bing for Bassett-Lowke, this scarce gauge II LNWR electric 4-6-2 tank locomotive is finished in original black livery. Note the crazing to the finish caused by age. Circa 1920.

*£450 — £600*

55 A Bing for Bassett Lowke gauge I 4-4-2 clockwork locomotive '44' finished in 'L&NWR' black livery, red and white lining. 40.6 cm long.

*£250 — £350*

56 Both large and impressive, this 1920s Bassett-Lowke live steam gauge II locomotive is complete with twin outside slide valve cylinders, regulator, water gauge glass, boiler blow-down, hand water pump and reversing lever. (Oversized whistle possibly not original.) Finished in early Midland maroon, it is complete with its tender with water and fuel spaces. 67.4 cm long.

*£400 — £600*

57 A gauge I 4-4-2 Precursor tank locomotive by Bassett-Lowke. Electric mechanism converted to centre rail pick up. It is painted in 'L&NWR' black livery. Circa 1920. 42 cm long. Attractive.

*£250 — £350*

58 Though not mint, this fine 4-6-2 tank locomotive by Marklin in gauge I is a sought after piece. This model carries a 'Gamage' trade mark. The livery, slightly retouched, is in 'L&NWR' black lined red and white. Clockwork. 42 cm overall.

*£300 — £400*

59 An electric gauge I 4-4-0 loco complete with headlamp and pointed smoke box door (for the Continental market), finished in black lined red and white. This model dates from the mid-1920s. 33 cm long. Note the Bing trade mark on cab. Also shown is a Marklin tender from the same period. 20.2 cm long.

*£150 — £200 (loco)*
*£20 — £40 (tender)*

60 A carpet toy, this German made miniature ½ in. gauge train set comprises a 'George the Fifth' 4-4-0 loco in L&NWR black livery with matching tender, 12.8 cm, together with two passenger coaches and van, each 8 cm long. Unusual. Circa 1920.

*£40 — £60 (as shown)*

61 The 'Orion' 4-4-0 express locomotive No. 1977, this clockwork gauge I model of German manufacture has an articulated six-wheeled tender for tight radius curves. Circa 1915-25. 52 cm overall.

*£250 — £400*

62 Made by Bing, and marketed by Bassett-Lowke, this gauge I electric 'George the Fifth' 4-4-0 locomotive is finished in original L&NWR black livery lined red and white. This model has detachable headlamps and sprung buffers. With tender 56 cm.

*£200 — £300*

63 Finished in GER dark blue livery and lined black edged red, this gauge 0 electric Bassett-Lowke 4-4-0 locomotive No. 1883 has a brass cabside number plate. Seen here with its tender having an incorrect Hornby coupling, the 'GER' lettering gilt shaded red. 36.2 cm overall.

*£400 — £475*

64 Bing made for Bassett-Lowke, a good 'Atlantic' 0 gauge, clockwork 4-4-2 locomotive No. 1442 with its six-wheeled matching tender lettered 'GNR' in gilt. 1920s. 39.4 cm overall. A good example.

*£400 — £500*

65 A crisp example of a 'George the Fifth' gauge 0 clockwork 4-4-0 locomotive by Bing for Bassett-Lowke. This particular model is in black livery and was very popular in the 1920s; a more detailed de luxe version exists by the same maker. 41.3 cm overall.

*£80 — £120 (standard)*
*£130 — £150 (de luxe)*

66 Bing made for Bassett-Lowke, this clockwork No. 504 'Mercury' bears a striking resemblance to the Bing 'George the Fifth' in the previous illustration. In fact it is the same pressing but with different livery and considerably scarcer.

*£150 — £200*

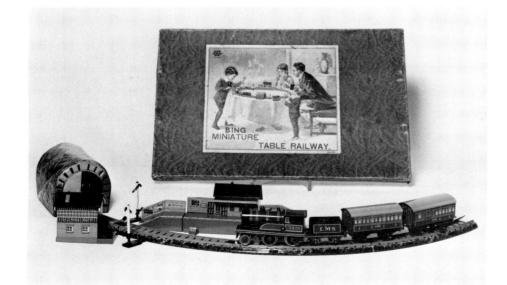

67 There can be no doubt that the original box adds a delightful new dimension to this 00 gauge clockwork railway set of the mid-1920s. The label depicts a doting father directing operations in his comfortable middle-class dining room. The set comprises 2-4-0 clockwork locomotive, four-wheeled tender, two coaches, a signal box, a station, a tunnel, two signals and a quantity of lithographed track. Almost mint condition.

*£150 — £180 (as shown)*
*£60 — £80 (in sound condition without box)*

35

68 Slightly earlier, Bing table railway set in clockwork 00 gauge and comprising a 'LNWR' 2-4-0 tank engine, 10.2 cm, two passenger coaches, guard's van, a station, a tunnel, four signals, two telegraph poles and a quantity of track with lithographed sleepers and track bed. The box showing signs of age. Circa 1923.

*£150 — £180*

69 Though its original box has suffered, this Bing 0 gauge 'GWR' passenger train set remains fresh. Intended to satisfy the cheaper end of the market and produced c.1925.

*£60 — £80 (with original box)*

70 00 gauge clockwork 2-4-0 tank locomotive in 'LMS' red livery, bearing Bing trade mark 'BW Bavaria', shown together with sectional Bing main platform. Circa 1925. Loco 10.2 cm.

*£20 — £30 (loco)*

71 Items from a Bing miniature railway set include a 2-4-0 00 gauge clockwork locomotive, a level crossing, a signal box and a signal. Circa 1925.

*£20 — £30 (loco)*
*£4 — £6 (crossing)*
*£6 — £10 (signal box)*

72 Further table railway items by Bing in 00 gauge, a clockwork 2-4-0 tank engine in 'L&NWR' black livery, a four-wheeled coach, a 'GWR' tank engine, an open 'L&NER' goods wagon, a set of buffer stops, an engine shed and a turnstile gatehouse.

*£20 — £30 (each loco)*     *£1 — £2 (buffer stop)*
*£3 — £5 (coach)*     *£8 — £12 (engine shed)*
*£2 — £4 (open wagon)*     *£6 — £8 (gatehouse)*

73 A Bing electric gauge I 4-4-0 locomotive No. 2663, 'George the Fifth' finished in black lined red and cream, tender not shown. 56.5 cm overall. Circa 1920.

*£200 — £250*

74 A good gauge I electric 4-4-2 tank locomotive in 'LB&SCR' dark green livery. 42 cm overall. Probably by Marklin.

*£300 — £400*

75 A well preserved 1920s gauge 0 4 volt electric train set by Bing. Bavarian style loco, carriages 'L&NWR' type with opening doors. Note '0-35' to cab. Locomotive 19.5 cm long.

*£60 — £100 (set as shown)*

76 From the 'cheaper' end of the early 1920s live steam range comes this 0 gauge 0-4-0 tank locomotive in 'LNER' green livery, No. 265. Made by Bowman, these models are invariably simple and unsophisticated but very functional. The paint damage is obvious, but understandable.

*£75 — £100*

77 A Hornby LNER 4-4-4 gauge 0 clockwork tank locomotive. Black livery with gilt lining. Circa 1925.

*£100 — £140*

78 A distressed but restorable Hornby 4-4-0 gauge 0 clockwork locomotive and tender. Note metal fatigue to wheels. Circa 1927.

*£40 — £60*

79 Typifying the semi-scale cheaper models, this gauge 0 'Duke of York' tender in unusually good condition bears the Bassett-Lowke trade mark, finishing in Midland maroon livery. Clockwork mechanism 3 lever operation. Circa 1927. 37.5 cm overall. These models were available in green livery and alternative numbers may be encountered.

*£100 — £130*

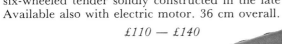

80 A well finished model by Hornby, and to scale, this 0 gauge clockwork 4-4-0 'LMS' compound locomotive and six-wheeled tender solidly constructed in the late 1930s. Available also with electric motor. 36 cm overall.

*£110 — £140*

81 Not faithful to detail (wheel configuration, etc.) a Hornby's 'Lord Nelson' clockwork gauge 0 4-4-2 locomotive together with its six-wheeled tender. An 'enjoyed' toy, as the dents and scratches testify. Collectors are reminded that metal fatigue on wheels is common, though replacements are still available. Semi-scale, lacking detail of previous model. Note smoke deflectors indicating later model.

*£50 — £75 (as shown)*
*£80 — £110 (sound order)*

82 Handsome, scarce and desirable, Hornby's Eton 4-4-0 electric gauge 0 locomotive and tender. One of the most sought after models from Hornby's late 1930s range. Announced in Hornby 1938-9 catalogue. (See also Colour Plate 5, page 31.)

*£200 — £300*

83 A Metropolitan train by Bing, 18 volt electric gauge 0 with overhead twin conductors, centre rail pick up. The four-wheeled locomotive is finished in maroon with detailing in yellow. Late 1920s. 23 cm long. Shown together with two Bing bogie coaches each 23 cm long.

*£140 — £180*

84 Complete with 'full' Walschaerts valve gear, this 1930s Marklin gauge 0 European 20 volt electric 4-6-2 express locomotive is finished in black lined gilt with red underframes. The matching tender has two four-wheeled bogies. 49.5 cm overall. Also shown with a Marklin passenger bogie coach lined and lettered in gilt. 40.6 cm.

*£750 — £900 (loco and tender)     £70 — £90 (coach)*

85 A mid-1930s 4-8-2 gauge 0 Marklin 20 volt locomotive with 'full' Walschaerts valve gear, pipe and handrail details, eight-wheeled bogie tender. 58.5 cm. Also shown are a similar period Marklin brake coach No. 19440, and a passenger bogie coach finished in maroon with 'Mitropa' and 'Berlin Stuttgart Speisewagen'. Both 40.5 cm long.

*£1,000 — £1,400 (loco and tender)     £80 — £100 (brake coach)     £80 — £100 (passenger coach)*

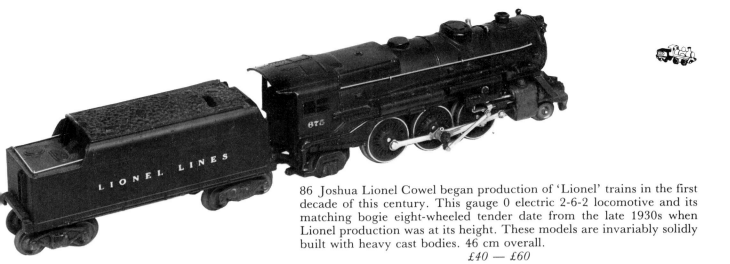

86 Joshua Lionel Cowel began production of 'Lionel' trains in the first decade of this century. This gauge 0 electric 2-6-2 locomotive and its matching bogie eight-wheeled tender date from the late 1930s when Lionel production was at its height. These models are invariably solidly built with heavy cast bodies. 46 cm overall.

*£40 — £60*

87 Obviously American, this Lionel New York Central diesel locomotive is electrically operated. It is gauge 0 and shown here with two streamlined carriages, one being a 'silver dawn' observation car. Circa 1940.

*£130 — £160*

88 Louis Marx North American tinplate range was extensive with an eye to the mass cheap market of the immediate pre- and post-war periods. The average collector may find many models 'tinny'. This Commodore Vanderbilt gauge 0 clockwork locomotive and tender with its 'Canadian Pacific' passenger coach is a typical example.

*£40 — £60*

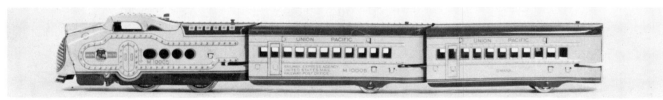

89 Futuristic, fun and 'flat', a Marx clockwork 'Union Pacific' train set in gauge 0. Note articulated connection of two-wheeled carriages and 'tab' construction.

*£40 — £60*

90 The tank transporter saves this electric streamlined locomotive from mediocrity. Tender missing. The tank itself is again typical of the cheaper Marx tinplate toys.

*£20 — £30 (loco and baggage car)*
*£30 — £40 (with tank transporter)*

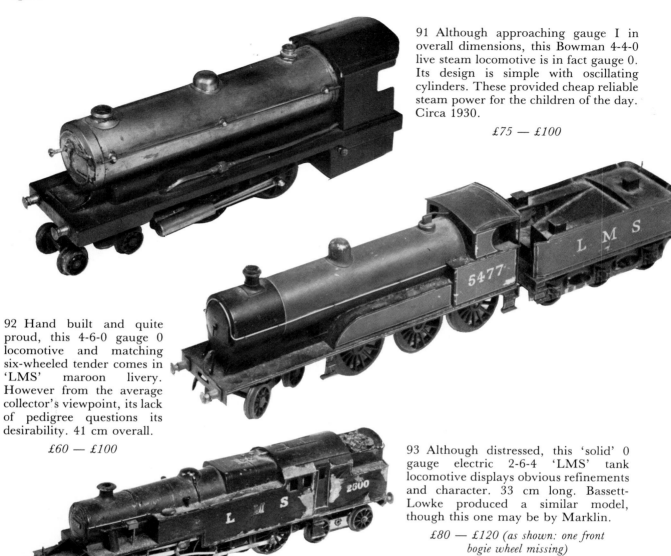

91 Although approaching gauge I in overall dimensions, this Bowman 4-4-0 live steam locomotive is in fact gauge 0. Its design is simple with oscillating cylinders. These provided cheap reliable steam power for the children of the day. Circa 1930.

*£75 — £100*

92 Hand built and quite proud, this 4-6-0 gauge 0 locomotive and matching six-wheeled tender comes in 'LMS' maroon livery. However from the average collector's viewpoint, its lack of pedigree questions its desirability. 41 cm overall.

*£60 — £100*

93 Although distressed, this 'solid' 0 gauge electric 2-6-4 'LMS' tank locomotive displays obvious refinements and character. 33 cm long. Bassett-Lowke produced a similar model, though this one may be by Marklin.

*£80 — £120 (as shown: one front bogie wheel missing)*

94 A 'County of Northampton' No. 3410, 4-4-0 locomotive and tender, gauge II, live steam spirit fired, by Bassett-Lowke, reversing gear, whistle, etc., in original GWR green livery with black and white lining. 60 cm overall. Shown here together with two clerestory roof coaches and GWR three section station.

*£400 — £600 (loco and tender)*
*£40 — £60 (each coach)*

95 An 'enjoyed' Bassett Lowke gauge 0 live steam spirit fired 4-4-0 locomotive and six-wheeled tender. Finished in maroon livery lined black edged yellow. Note the tender housing fuel tank and controls. Circa 1923. 40 cm overall.

*£175 — £250*

96 The LMS compound locomotive was manufactured by many companies. This particular Bassett-Lowke example is 2½ in. gauge coal fired live steam. Note the splasher plates bearing 'Lady Iris'. Finished in 'LMS' maroon livery, it has a copper superheated boiler mounted on springs. Circa 1930. 81 cm overall.

*£600 — £800*

97 A Bassett-Lowke gauge I 2-6-0 electric locomotive finished in green 'LNER' livery and numbered 33, together with its matching tender. Circa 1930. 63.5 cm overall.

*£400 — £500*

98 By Bassett-Lowke, this 4-6-0 electric locomotive in gauge 0 is finished in green 'LNER' livery with the name plate 'Arsenal' together with a six-wheeled tender. Circa 1930. 43.2 cm long. Scarce.

*£300 — £400*

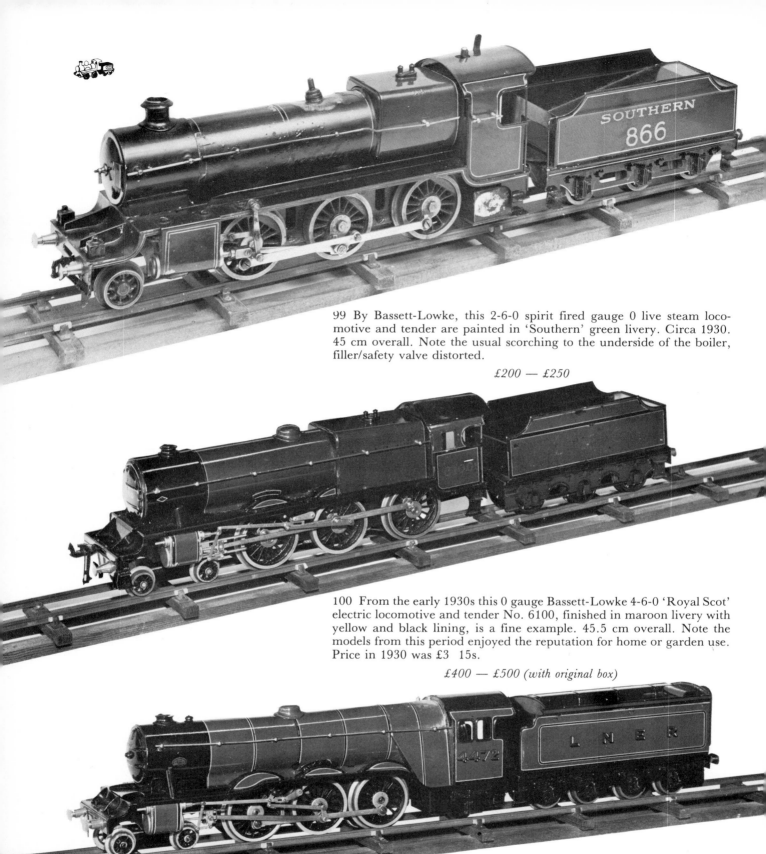

99 By Bassett-Lowke, this 2-6-0 spirit fired gauge 0 live steam locomotive and tender are painted in 'Southern' green livery. Circa 1930.
45 cm overall. Note the usual scorching to the underside of the boiler,
filler/safety valve distorted.

*£200 — £250*

100 From the early 1930s this 0 gauge Bassett-Lowke 4-6-0 'Royal Scot'
electric locomotive and tender No. 6100, finished in maroon livery with
yellow and black lining, is a fine example. 45.5 cm overall. Note the
models from this period enjoyed the reputation for home or garden use.
Price in 1930 was £3  15s.

*£400 — £500 (with original box)*

101 The forever famous 'Flying Scotsman', No. 4472, again from
Bassett-Lowke's 1930s range, gauge 0 electric, a sought after model by
collectors. Price in 1937 4 guineas, available with a choice of electric
motors, and in clockwork. 51 cm overall.

*£450 — £600 (with original box)*

102 Bassett-Lowke's 'Princess Royal' 4-6-2 electric gauge 0 locomotive and tender in 'LMS' maroon livery, No. 6200. 51 cm overall. A fine example of the immediate pre-war period.

*£300 — £400*

103 Introduced pre-war, this is a post-war version of the 'Super Enterprise' gauge 0 4-6-0 live steam spirit fired locomotive, in original eggshell black livery lined red. This model has a combined safety valve/filler plug, whistle, main steam valve and twin outside slide valve cylinders with slip eccentric reverse. Together with its BR lion transfer tender and with its original Bassett-Lowke box, this model was retailing at £13 7s. 8d. in the early 1950s. The pre-war price was £3 17s. 6d.

*£450 — £550*

104 From the mid-1930s and in lovely condition with its original box, this Bassett-Lowke 0 gauge electric 0-6-0 tank locomotive No. 78 is finished in black livery lined red and lettered 'LMS' in gilt shaded red. 24 cm.

*£180 — £220 (as shown)*
*£100 — £130 (sound example)*

105 A tank locomotive by Bassett-Lowke in gauge I having clockwork mechanism (also available in electric and steam). It is finished in original maroon livery with black and yellow lining and sprung buffers. 26.8 cm long. No. 112 (112 being the number of Bassett-Lowke's retail shop in High Holborn, London).

*£140 — £160*

106 Again introduced in the pre-war period, this sleek 'Mogul' gauge 0 live steam 2-6-0 locomotive together with its six-wheeled tender has a lion and wheel transfer, indicating a post-war model (also available in clock-work and electric). Finished in black. 46 cm long.

*£200 — £300*

107 The not uncommon 'Prince Charles' Bassett-Lowke gauge 0 4-4-0 clockwork locomotive together with its six-wheeled BR transfer tender. Circa 1950. 40 cm overall. Light paint damage but complete and attractive.

*£80 — £120*

108 Another 'Prince Charles'. Note similar paint scratches as on the previous item. Hand rail missing. 50,000-60,000 of this model were produced. Finished in BR green.

*£75 — £100*

109 From Italy comes this good electric 4-4-4-4 locomotive in gauge 0 with overhead twin collapsible conductors, perspex windows, headlamps, etc. This model finished in khaki with brown features. Marked 'Elettren'. Mid-1950s. 43 cm overall.

*£200 — £300*

110 Marklin's contribution to the 00 market included this 4-6-2 German loco-motive with eight-wheeled bogie tender which is shown facing in the wrong direction. It is well engineered and of the usual Marklin high quality.

*£25 — £30*

In 1938 Hornby introduced the Hornby 'Dublo' range, a development its founder Frank Hornby (1863-1936) would have been proud of since it allowed for a continually growing 'system' which was impractical in 0 gauge. Already there is great demand for marked 'Dublo' pieces and scarce models, modifications and numbers make it a collecting world in itself. All the following Hornby models shown are electric 00 gauge.

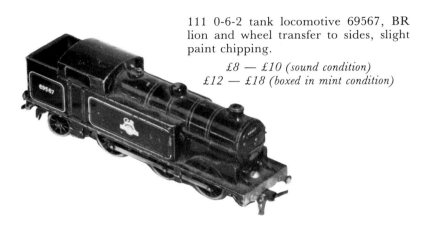

111 0-6-2 tank locomotive 69567, BR lion and wheel transfer to sides, slight paint chipping.

*£8 — £10 (sound condition)*
*£12 — £18 (boxed in mint condition)*

112 4-6-0 'Bristol Castle' No. 7013 and six-wheeled tender.

*£10 — £12 (sound condition)*
*£18 — £25 (boxed in mint condition)*

113 4-6-2 'Golden Fleece' No. 60030 locomotive and tender, shown here with original slightly soiled box.

*£12 — £18 (as shown)*
*£8 — £10 (unboxed)*

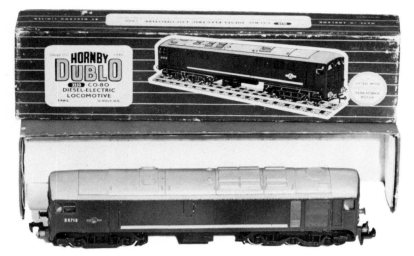

114 With its three-pair and two-pair wheel configuration, a Co-Bo diesel electric locomotive D5713 with original box. Note three-rail model.

*£20 — £30 (boxed)*
*£10 — £15 (sound condition)*

115 Another Co-Bo locomotive D5702, with original box. Note two-rail model.

*£20 — £30 (boxed)*
*£10 — £15 (sound condition)*

116 A Dublo Co-Co (twelve-wheeled) diesel electric locomotive.

*£20 — £30 (boxed)*
*£12 — £18 (sound condition)*

117 A Dublo 2-6-4 tank locomotive 80054.

*£12 — £18 (boxed)*
*£8 — £12 (sound condition)*

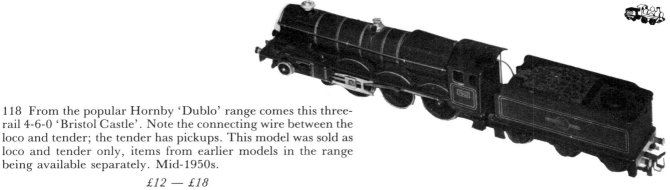

118 From the popular Hornby 'Dublo' range comes this three-rail 4-6-0 'Bristol Castle'. Note the connecting wire between the loco and tender; the tender has pickups. This model was sold as loco and tender only, items from earlier models in the range being available separately. Mid-1950s.

*£12 — £18*

119 A Hornby 'Dublo' two-rail 4-8-0 heavy goods locomotive and tender. This model was issued in both two- and three-rail form in the early 1960s. Note the number 48109.

*£12 — £18*

120 A similar Hornby 'Dublo' locomotive and tender, this time three-rail. Circa 1958. Note the number 48158.

*£12 — £18*

121 A selection of H0 and 00 items including a Triang 'Lord of the Isles', a Continental 4-6-4 tank locomotive, a Triang Hornby 'Caledonian' railway 4-2-2 boxed, a Hornby 'Dublo' 0-6-2 tank loco 'LNER' green livery, a Graham Farish 4-6-0 locomotive and tender and a H0 Jones Cockerill 85 tonne crane set in original box. Circa 1950-65.

*£10 — £30 (each)*

# Rolling Stock and Railway Accessories

Directly coupled to the interest shown in toy locomotives, collectors will find a wide range of rolling stock available. The visual attractiveness of these accessories can independently form a worthwhile and interesting collection.

Early examples of four-wheeled rolling stock are generally colourful, being hand enamelled and lined. Later examples are better detailed, some bogie coaches having corridor connections, interior detail and opening doors. Even hinged roofs were sometimes provided enabling passengers to be inserted. A range of figures were produced by various companies for use with railways. Many carriages have Continental style steps to doors, a feature required on the Continent where platforms are not raised.

By the World War I period advertising had appeared on rolling stock, petrol tankers, etc., and in the 1920s and 1930s a wide range of trade names was available.

Again gauges on some early coaches can be determined by lithographed numerals (see introduction to Early Models in Train section).

*Colour Plate 6. A rake of three gauge 0 Bing bogie coaches in 'LMS' livery, comprising two 1st/3rd passenger coaches and brake van, opening doors, automatic couplings. Circa 1930. 24.5 cm long each.*

*£60 — £80 (each)*

122 An extremely interesting accessory for early model trains was this 'Railway Smash' by Marklin which comprised two coaches and a brake van. Very scarce.

*£1,200 — £1,500*

123 Shown here Bassett-Lowke's original advertisement for the 'Railway Smash' (1905-6 catalogue). A toy that deviates from the general straightforward approach of Edwardian toys.

124 In the scarce gauge II, this Bing petrol tanker has a ladder and external framework around the tank. Marked 'Petroleum Comp'. Circa 1910. 16 cm. Note non-original coupling on left of picture.

*£20 — £30*
*£15 — £20 (gauge 0 or I)*

126 Delightful with its corrugated canopy, this gauge II breakdown crane has a crank wound turntable. 31 cm.

*£25 — £40*

125 Again in gauge II comes this Bing side tipping wagon. Circa 1910. 16 cm.

*£20 — £25*

127 First class still, in spite of paint damage and rust, this Bing gauge II six-wheeled carriage is still structurally complete. Circa 1910. 27 cm. Note centre pair of wheels is mounted to enable negotiation of tight curves.

*£50 — £75*

128 Complete with its fitted interior, this gauge II Marklin Continental clerestory bogie passenger coach dates from c.1903. Finished as a sleeping car with dark maroon body, detailing in chocolate and gilding and having a slate blue roof. 38 cm. The example shown has been partially repainted.

*£250 — £350*

129 A selection of railway items by Marklin which include an attractive station, c.1895-1900, with real coloured glass windows which show up delightfully when illuminated by two candles. Note the chimneys, decorated roof and arched entrance.

*£120 — £150*

130 The value of this gauge I Bing carriage is enhanced by the fact that it is a dining saloon and as such is mounted on twelve wheels (six-wheeled bogies). Finished in 'L&NWR' livery. 52 cm long. Illustrated in Bassett-Lowke's 1912/13 catalogue, price 12s. 6d. (62½ p).

*£60 — £90*

131 Representative of the range of accessories is this unusual gauge I 'L&NWR' post office bogie coach, complete with operational mailbag collection equipment tripped by a lever under the coach striking a special track fitting; a section of this track is illustrated here. Possibly by Bing and retailed by Bassett-Lowke. Circa 1915. 43 cm overall.

*£60 — £90*

132 Probably pre-World War I, this Marklin 'L&NWR' 1st/3rd bogie passenger carriage in gauge II retains much of its original finish. Note the fine quality lithographic work to the sides. Red printed trade mark to underside. 42 cm long.

*£40 — £60*

133 Again by Marklin in similar gauge, this fine bogie corridor Pullman (later named 'Cynthia') displays attractive painted upper window lights. Note the presence of steps indicating Continental use. Circa 1920.

*£70 — £100*

134 Typically Bing, in scarce gauge II, this 3rd class brake has well lithographed sides with double opening doors, handrails, lamps, etc., mansell type bogie wheels. Note the absence of one ventilator. In 'Midland' livery, this model was first made for Bassett Lowke in 1919. 47 cm long.

*£50 — £60*

135 A similar Bing 1st and 3rd class passenger carriage, this particular model is well repainted but this factor detracts from its value.

*£30 — £40*

136 A Carette gauge I short wheelbase bogie coach with clerestory roof to 1st and 3rd class compartments. Chocolate and cream livery. First quarter of the 20th century. 30.5 cm long.

*£60 — £80*

137 Two gauge I Carette passenger carriages, one finished in 'Midland' maroon livery, the other in CIWR chocolate and cream livery, both having clerestory roofs. Circa 1920.

*£50 — £75 (each)*

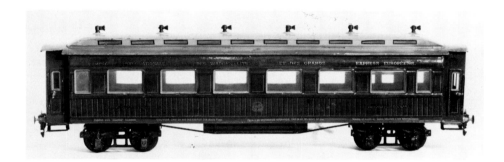

138 A fine gauge I Marklin bogie CIWR (Continental) sleeping car having detachable clerestory roof with original cream shaded grey finish, detailing in orange. Teak livery, grey underframe, unfitted interior. Circa 1920. 53 cm overall. Very scarce.

*£350 — £450*

139 A Bassett-Lowke LMS gauge 0 Royal Mail van with track operated catch net. Offered in the October 1923 Bassett-Lowke catalogue without ground apparatus at £1 2. 6d. or with ground apparatus at £1 10s. Note the 'Lowke' trade mark to chassis. The maker's name is printed under communicating door.

*£50 — £75*

140 Note the heavy paint damage to this Bing gauge 0 'GWR' dining carriage. This model introduced by Bing in 1926 is interesting as it has interior detail tables, chairs, etc., and a hinged roof allowing passengers to be inserted.

*£18 — £25*

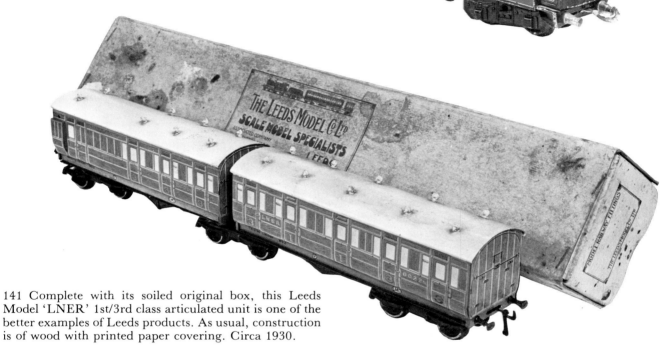

141 Complete with its soiled original box, this Leeds Model 'LNER' 1st/3rd class articulated unit is one of the better examples of Leeds products. As usual, construction is of wood with printed paper covering. Circa 1930.

*£30 — £40*

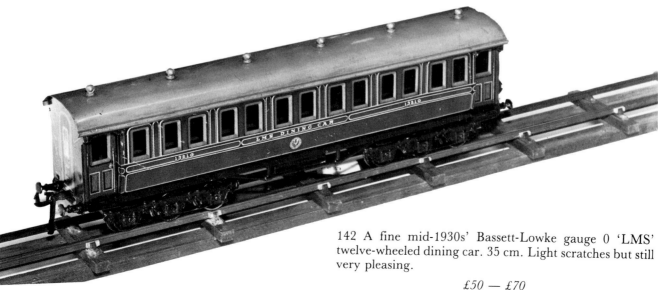

142 A fine mid-1930s' Bassett-Lowke gauge 0 'LMS' twelve-wheeled dining car. 35 cm. Light scratches but still very pleasing.

*£50 — £70*

143 A pre-war gauge 0 Hornby four-wheeled 1st/3rd 'GWR' passenger carriage with opening doors, early pattern underframe but note the later automatic couplings.

*£8 — £12*

144 A pre-war 'LMS' Hornby gauge 0 timber truck (note early pre-war models have cut away suspension details); a Bing 'Pratts' motor spirit tanker (wheels missing) and a Hornby 'NE' open wagon.

*£3 — £5 (truck)*
*£4 — £6 (tanker)*
*£3 — £5 (wagon)*

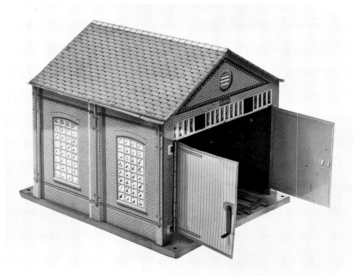

145 A Hornby pre-war gauge 0 'LNER' snow plough. Note the sliding door and voided underframe which indicates an early example.

*£20 — £30*

146 A good example of a Hornby pre-war No. 1A engine shed sold for 10s. 6d. (52½ p) in 1937. More elaborate versions existed, some with electric lighting.

*£20 — £30*

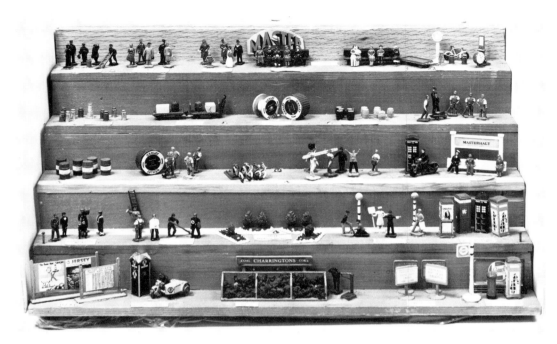

147 Of the great many accessories available for 00 layouts, Master Models produced an extensive selection of die-cast items some of which are shown here.

*Under £1 per piece*

148 A Selection of 00 gauge rolling stock including seven Hornby tin bodied 'Dublo' carriages, restaurant car, etc., two Trix carriages and six items of goods wagons, tankers, etc. All mid-1950s.

*£4 — £6 (Hornby carriage)*
*£3 — £5 (Trix carriage)*
*£2 — £3 (goods wagon)*
*£2 — £3 (petrol tanker)*

# Stationary Steam Engines, Steam Toys and Accessories

The Industrial Revolution and its dependence on steam must have greatly influenced the introduction of stationary steam engine toys, which were commercially produced from the late 19th century.

A wide variety of sizes and quality were produced and both horizontal and vertical boilers are encountered together with numerous cylinder permutations. Most of the German toy manufacturers produced these more adventurous and potentially harmful toys, together with a vast range of ingenious accessories to be driven by these engines.

On the sophisticated models pressure gauges, level glasses and oilers will be found although on simple models only a safety valve (essential) and whistle may be present. Many models were realistically produced with impressed brick detail on chimneys, etc., and are usually still found in working order. Methylated spirit was most popular for heating the boiler but the use of solid fuel is sometimes encountered.

Although such toys are still produced today, most companies ceased production of these engines before the Second World War.

*Value Point*
Unsteamed examples with box and instructions + + + +

*Colour Plate 7. An ingenious Doll et Cie steam accessory in the form of a water powered saw mill. The pumped water delivered to the wheel drives the saw. Note 'DC' trade mark to side of base. (See also 164, page 63.)*

*Colour Plate 8. One of Bing's steam accessories, the blacksmith is driven by a pulley from the back and has articulated arms and head. The anvil from his workbench is missing. Circa 1920-25. 12 cm high. (See also 165, page 63.)*

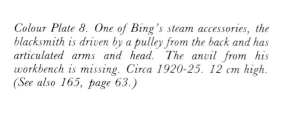

149 This portable steam engine by Bing has heavy forward mounted flywheel, single cylinder, whistle, etc. The level glass, governor and chimney are missing. Early 20th century. 25.5. cm long.

*£250 — £300*

150 A good early live steam portable engine by Bing having side mounted single cylinder with slide valve, forward mounted flywheel complete with whistle, burner, etc. The chimney is missing. The flywheel and road wheels are finished in good original dark chocolate with red lining. An early printed trade mark indicates circa first decade 20th century. 24 cm long. A desirable item.

*£200 — £300*

151 A fine Marklin portable steam engine complete with water gauge glass, whistle, safety valve, etc. Repainted. Note original brass maker's plate reading 'G.M. & Cie', Wurtlemberg D5½'. Almost certainly earlier than indicated by label. 24.2 cm long.

*£450 — £550*

152 An interestingly early twin cylinder vertical hot air engine very probably by Carette, having blued heating chamber and finished in original dark chocolate Circa 1900. 36.8 cm high.

*£225 — £275*

153 Produced for the true steam enthusiast, this fine and rare Marklin twin cylinder steam plant was produced in the first decade of this century, superbly detailed with handrails, steps to gallery, lubricators, level glass, safety valve, etc. Note the belt driven dynamo. Baseplate 68 by 37 cm.

*£2,000 — £3,000*

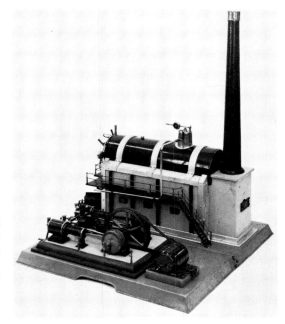

154 Extremely rare, this important model steam plant is possibly the largest to appear in the catalogues of the toy manufacturer, being 85 by 89 cm and 113 cm high. Note tidy layout with twin cylinders, dynamo, governor, etc., and two piece baseplate. Made by Marklin in the first decade of the 20th century.

*£1,000 — £1,500*

155 Lacking the power of steam, this fine and early Ernst Plank engine is powered by hot air and possesses period charm. Here shown with a selection of accessories affixed to wooden base. First decade 20th century. Just visible is a Gamages plate on engine base.

*£150 — £180*

156 By Marklin, this good and early live steam engine has vertical boiler and is well detailed with water level glass, pressure gauge, whistle, filler, lubricators, etc. Finished in good original black paintwork lined in blue. 28 cm high, mounted on tinplate base 37 cm square. Note Marklin attached metal trade mark on boiler side.

*£250 — £300*

157 This well detailed vertical steam engine was produced by Bing. Note auxiliary side mounted cylinder operating feed pump. Of robust construction and finished in original black and red paintwork. Circa 1912. 36.2 cm high.

*£120 — £160*

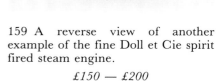

158 A well engineered spirit fired steam engine by Doll et Cie, note attention to detail, lubricators, taps, etc. Finished in good original black livery to green and vermilion lining. Second decade 20th century. 44.5 cm high.

*£200 — £300*

159 A reverse view of another example of the fine Doll et Cie spirit fired steam engine.

*£150 — £200*

161 An Ernst Plank horizontal steam engine fitted with slip eccentric reversing mechanism pressure gauge, water level glass, whistle, etc., and mounted on raised tin base with imitation tiled surface. Second decade 20th century.

*£60 — £80*

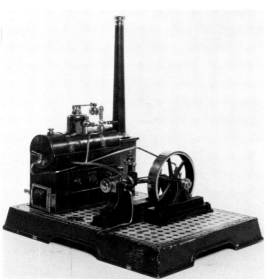

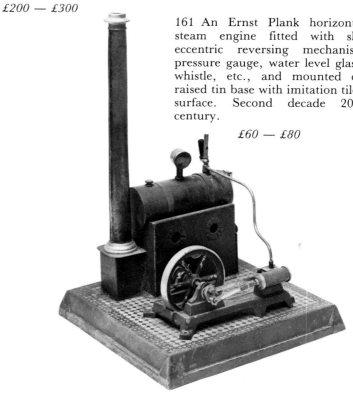

160 Made for Gamages, this Marklin horizontal steam plant has attractively appointed boiler fitted with regulator, whistle, safety valve, etc. Finished in original black highlighted in maroon and turquoise. Second decade 20th century. 25.4 by 34.3 cm.

*£175 — £250*

162 A tinplate ferris wheel accessory by Doll et Cie having three pivoted seats with painted composition passengers. Finished in powder blue and white with scarlet and crimson lining. First decade 20th century. 16 cm high.

*£30 — £50*

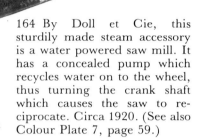

164 By Doll et Cie, this sturdily made steam accessory is a water powered saw mill. It has a concealed pump which recycles water on to the wheel, thus turning the crank shaft which causes the saw to reciprocate. Circa 1920. (See also Colour Plate 7, page 59.)

*£40 — £60*

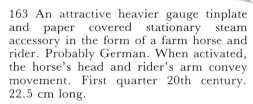

163 An attractive heavier gauge tinplate and paper covered stationary steam accessory in the form of a farm horse and rider. Probably German. When activated, the horse's head and rider's arm convey movement. First quarter 20th century. 22.5 cm long.

*£15 — £25*

165 In contrast to 164 this Bing steam accessory relies on lithography to indicate depth. The blacksmith's head and arms are moved when a hidden pulley is coupled to the steam engine (anvil and rod missing). Circa 1920-25. (See also Colour Plate 8, page 59.)

*£25 — £40*

166 Of unknown manufacture, this big wheel accessory with six cars is of cheaply made flimsy construction. Circa 1920s.

*£18 — £25*

168 Note the unusual attachment to chimney on this good Bing steam plant, possibly a condensing tank mounted on tinplate base with electric generator. Note terminals and on/off switch. Second decade 20th century. 33 cm square.

*£200 — £300*

167 A good spirit fired steam plant by Doll et Cie. Single cylinder, slip eccentric revers-ing mechanism incorporating imitation regulator, water level glass, pressure gauge, weight operated safety valve, whistle, drain tap, etc. Note well defined imitation brickwork, shown here with a Doll et Cie vertical saw bench accessory. Circa 1920.

*£175 — £200 (steam plant)*
*£12 — £20 (saw bench)*

169 Very unusual, this twin cylinder Doll et Cie steam plant has a horizontal boiler with upright vertical cylinders and comes complete with usual fittings. Circa 1920. Mounted on tin baseplate 33 by 25.5 cm.

*£200 — £300*

170 By Bing, this vertical steam engine has a single cylinder, regulator, level glass, safety valve (lacking weight), cast fire box door bearing GBN trade mark. Circa 1920.

£200 — £300

171 A Doll et Cie single cylinder vertical steam engine having safety valve, level glass, governor, etc. Note repairs to exhaust pipe. Circa 1920.

£175 — £250

172 A single cylinder vertical steam engine by Bing, having whistle, lubricators, etc. Finished in black and red with lacquered brightwork. 33 cm high.

£150 — £200

173 By Falk, another vertical single cylinder steam engine with brightwork finished. Circa 1920. 31.2 cm high.

£175 — £250

174 A good vertical Marklin steam engine. Note pierced chimney top and Marklin trade plate on boiler. 1920s. 40 cm. high.

£100 — £150

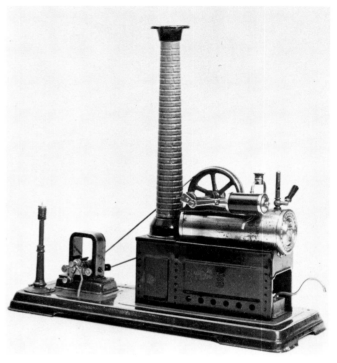

176 A fine example of a Bing horizontal steam engine and generator (dynamo). Although not clear in photograph, function of dynamo is confirmed by 'screw-in' early pattern bulb. Note impressed Bing trade marks to boiler and firebox side. Circa 1925. 31 cm wide, 31 cm high.

*£100 — £150*

175 By Doll et Cie, this model retains much original finish increasing desirability to collectors — original mottled maroon and black with orange lining. Slip eccentric reverse pressure gauge, whistle, etc. A good typical example of the period. Circa 1920. 21.5 by 19 cm.

*£50 — £75*

177 Unusual in configuration, this Ernst Plank hot air engine uses two cylinders. Although these engines functioned well they lacked the power of the steam engine and could not be relied upon to drive larger accessories, hence these are scarcer, though this is not, as yet reflected in the price. Applied oval Plank trade mark.

*£50 — £80*

178 Produced by Bing for universal use, these steam engine accessories add interest and realism for the steam engine collector. Illustrated here is a band saw (saw missing) and a drill. Note Bing trade mark attached to wooden baseplate. Circa 1920-30.

*£10 — £12 (each)*

179 A Bing vertical single cylinder stationary steam engine shown here with original box, together with a Bing transfer shaft, circular saw with box, and a power hammer. Note multi-lingual Bing labels to boxes. Late 1920s. Box 28 cm high.

*£25 — £40 (engine)*
*£4 — £6 (transfer shaft)*
*£12 — £15 (saw)*
*£8 — £12 (hammer)*

181 Produced to power Meccano models, this vertical steam engine has reversing single cylinder motion driving through reduction gear to main shaft. Most Meccano collectors preferred the convenience of clockwork or electric motors to propel their models, hence steam types are scarce. Circa 1930.

*£25 — £35*

180 Unmarked, these stationary steam accessories consist of: centre, hammer and anvil with variable speed (boxed); right, a single speed hammer; left, a rotary grain grinder.

*£12 — £18 (variable speed hammer and anvil)*
*£6 — £8 (single speed hammer)*
*£10 — £15 (grain grinder)*

# Novelty Toys

**Early to circa 1930 Models**

The ingenuity of the German and French manufacturers at the turn of the century contributes to the desirable qualities of these toys. All manner of mechanical creatures with clockwork mechanisms concealed within their tinplate bodies exemplify this 'Golden Age'. Many conduct several motions by incorporating cams and cranked shafts. The majority of these toys were inexpensive and would have been disposed of when the clockwork motors failed although these were fairly robust. Again early items were hand enamelled and later items lithographed. Both tab and slot and soldered construction will be encountered, and some models, particularly Martin products, have cloth clothing.

Because of their thin tinplate construction these models are unfortunately subject to rust and light oiling is better treatment for this than overpainting.

The Second World War with its requirement for metal will have contributed to the scarcity of these models.

*Value Point*
With box + + + +

**Post-1930 Models**

The influence of popular cartoon characters is evident in this period, dominated as it was by the imagination of Walt Disney which was soon translated to popular toys. Schuco, too, became a dominant force with their clockwork tinplate cloth covered animal figures.

The Japanese and others began production of toys which, in some cases, were futuristic but in others mere copies of earlier successful toys.

The German ingenuity and influence was subsiding under the pressure of cheap, less inspired toys of American mass production.

*Value Point*
With box + + + +

182 A rare tinplate push-along drummer boy mounted on one small and two large wheels, the small wheel connected to arms by wire causing drumming motion when pushed forward. Possibly French. Circa 1890. 14.5 cm high.

*£250 — £300*

183 Lehmann's 'Walking Down Broadway' couple has a flywheel driven mechanism concealed within the lady's skirt which causes the gentleman's legs to move. The lady has an orange dress and bonnet with cream bodice, the gentleman a brown jacket, cap and striped trousers. Circa 1896. 15 cm tall.

*£300 — £400*

184 Of unknown manufacture, but resembling a Martin product, this clockwork fireman is hand enamelled. The legs move in a realistic manner enabling the fireman to climb a ladder. Circa 1900. (See also Colour Plate 9, page 77.)

*£75 — £100*

185 A painted tinplate drawing clown. The seated figure facing easel holds a drawing stick in one hand and the turning handle at the rear causes cam operation of head and arm, thereby drawing a picture on the easel. The cams are interchangeable enabling different drawings to be executed. Shown right with fourteen cams. Made by Philip Vielmetter. Circa 1900.

*£500 — £600*

186 This hand enamelled tinplate clockwork soldier is finished in green with red piping and bearing pennant. Possibly a French or Russian soldier from the Boxer Rebellion. Probably by Martin. Circa 1900. 23 cm high.

*£220 — £280*

187 Note the FM trade mark on this climbing man. Hand painted with simulated hair, key at shoulder (note the similarity to climbing fireman, 184). Finished in light blue, ladder missing. Martin, France. Circa 1900. 18.5 cm high.

*£150 — £200*

188 Another Martin toy, this aggressive looking Chinaman wielding polearm and sword was probably influenced by the Boxer Rebellion. Hand enamelled and in Oriental tunic, trousers, etc. Clockwork. Circa 1900. 18 cm high.

*£250 — £300*

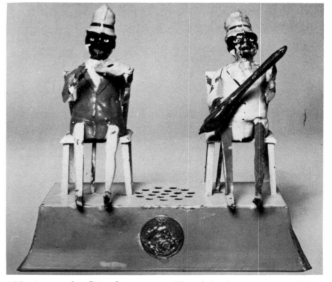

189 A Fernand Martin piano player with material clothes, imitation hair, etc. The seated figure with its clockwork activated body and arms gives the impression of playing the piano. Circa 1900. 13 cm wide.

*£150 — £200*

190 An early Günthermann 'Excelsior' toy, comprising two hand enamelled seated negroes, one playing violin (damaged) the other a banjo. The clockwork mechanism causes a melody to play from within base. 21 by 21.5 by 11.8 cm. Circa 1895. Scarce — note early circular trade mark to base.

*£600 — £800*

 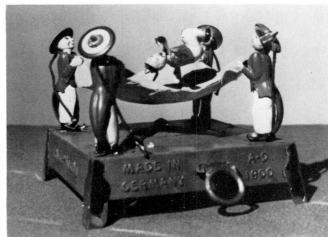

191 Five illustrations showing the activity of this Lehmann toy inspired by the Boxer Rebellion in China, 1900. Each pigtailed coolie (wearing hats emblazoned with national colour of nations involved — Great Britain, France, Russia and Japan) holds a corner of a blanket and appears to toss a Chinaman in the air. The ingenious motion is promoted by a concealed clockwork motor causing the figures to move forwards and back and on the fourth occasion to spring back violently tossing the figure, who is held to the centre of the blanket by his pigtail. A superb toy believed to be very rare. Circa 1900.

*£500 — £750*

192 Of incredibly simple construction, this 'Penny Toy' cyclist is of die-cast tin and wire construction; the front wheel is caused to spin by a length of string and the cyclist travels speedily upright by its gyroscopic action. Possibly English. The rider's coat and cap are finished in metallic blue. Circa 1900. 7.3 cm long.

*£20 — £30*

194 The 'Preacher and the Pulpit' tinplate toy by Martin displays traces of original applied trade mark at the centre of the pulpit. The preacher is dressed in a black material robe with white cravat (hat missing) and holds a text in one hand whilst the other hand rises and falls in benediction. Circa 1905-10. 24 cm high.

*£200 — £250*

193 This view of Lehmann's 'Man Da Rin' sedan chair clearly indicates a patent registration date of 1903. 18.5 cm long, 14 cm high. (See also Colour Plate 10, page 77.)

*£300 — £350*

195 A flywheel driven Lehmann ostrich cart, painted red, with seated driver. Simple friction drive to wheels causes the ostrich to walk in a realistic manner. First decade 20th century. 18 cm.

*£150 — £225*

196 Two versions of the Lehmann Am Pol tinplate tricycle having concealed clockwork mechanism driving rear wheels and causing driver's right arm to swing up and down. The parasol in the form of the Northern Hemisphere rotates. The model without the parasol shows patent dates. First decade 20th century. 13 cm long.

*£250 — £350*
*£150 — £200 (without parasol)*

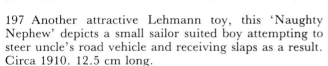

198 Difficult to find, this Bing 'Plunging Pike' shown here with original box has pressed tin body with simulated scales, painted grey-green with salmon pink underside. The mouth and gills are brown, white, pink and red (dorsal fin missing). Propulsion is provided by clockwork motor concealed within a watertight compartment and driving a four-bladed screw. 35.5 cm long. The fact that these plunging pikes dived and swam underwater contributes to their rarity as many would have been lost in ponds and rivers.

*£325 — £400*

197 Another attractive Lehmann toy, this 'Naughty Nephew' depicts a small sailor suited boy attempting to steer uncle's road vehicle and receiving slaps as a result. Circa 1910. 12.5 cm long.

*£275 — £350*

199 By Ernst Plank and clearly displaying a trade mark, this swimming fish has a pressed tinplate body with simulated scales, fins, gills and eyes with winding hole at side. The clockwork mechanism drives the propeller at tail. Finished in cream with pink and black detail. Circa 1910. 21 cm long. Not as realistic as Bing version.

*£200 — £250*

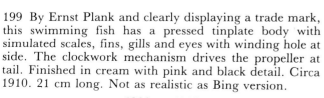

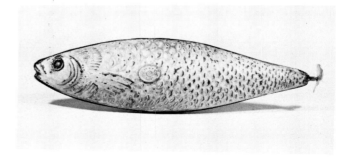

200  Balancing a propeller on his nose, this clockwork clown is of German origin. Note simple bent wire winder at waist. Circa 1910. 23 cm high.

*£50 — £80*

201  An unusual tinplate 'clown on ball' toy. The colourfully dressed figure seated astride a weighted ball retains an upright posture when the ball is rolled. Maker unknown. Circa 1910. 23 cm high.

*£140 — £180*

202  A classic toy, the bagatelle player was produced by various makers. The player keeps playing for as long as tension remains in the spring, while balls are recycled by the Archimedean screw spiral principle. Found in various colours. Circa 1910. 29.5 cm. long.

*£350 — £500*

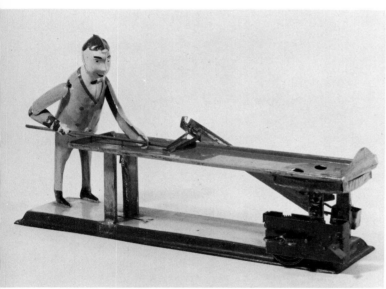

203  A string operated Lehmann mechanical flying bird having hand enamelled tinplate body with paper wings which were printed in imitation of feathers. Circa 1910. 18 cm long.

*£40 — £60*

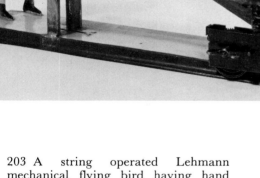

204  'Tut-Tut' was the name given to this horn blowing toy by Lehmann. The clockwork mechanism drives rear wheels and activates a bellows-operated horn held to driver's mouth. Finished in off-white with red detail, maroon seat. Circa 1910. 17 cm long.

*£200 — £300*

205 Another Lehmann product, this time the 'Li-La' horseless cab, having an ingenious clockwork mechanism which causes the driver to steer an erratic course, and one lady to swing her brolly causing communication hatch to open. The other lady attempts to discourage a begging dog which has a rotating head. Second decade 20th century. 14 cm long. Two examples, in different colours, are shown.

*£250 — £350*

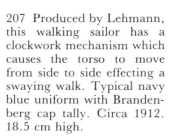

206 By Victor Bonnet et Cie, this tinplate musical clown dressed in material Pierrot suit, with bells attached to hands, feet and head, is operated by five keys, metal trade mark just visible on seat. French. Second decade 20th century. 26 cm high.

*£500 — £600*

207 Produced by Lehmann, this walking sailor has a clockwork mechanism which causes the torso to move from side to side effecting a swaying walk. Typical navy blue uniform with Brandenberg cap tally. Circa 1912. 18.5 cm high.

*£100 — £150*

208 Although almost unbelievable in concept, this vehicle toy entitled 'Anxious Bride' by Lehmann is based on an actual form of transport. The clockwork motor provides drive to the rear wheels of the tricycle, the lady passenger rises up and down waving her arms and handkerchief, and the chauffeur gives the impression of providing power through the pedals. Circa 1914. 21.5 cm long. This model is rare with original paper handkerchief.

*£400 — £500*

209 Another of Lehmann's ingenious mechanical toys is this crawling beetle. On this model wings flap and legs move in pairs. Finished in lithographed green, white, yellow, red and gilt. Circa 1915. 9.5 cm long.

*£80 — £120*

210 On initial inspection this crawling beetle appears identical to the previous item. However it bears a 'Ballerina' trade mark which indicates that it was produced by Richard and Carl Adam at an earlier date. It would appear that Lehmann used some of this company's designs. Circa 1900. 9.5 cm. long.

*£80 — £120*

211 Two examples of Lehmann's 'Zikra' bucking zebra; the clockwork motor within the clown's cart generates motion to the zebra causing the cart to tip in an alarming manner. Circa 1915. 18 cm long.

*£80 — £110 (reins missing, leg broken)*
*£120 — £150 (finer, complete example)*

212 A different application of design although retaining the same concept of motion as the previous example, this model by Lehmann was known as the 'Balky Mule'. Circa 1912. (See also Colour Plate 11, opposite.)

*£110 — £140*

Colour Plate 10. Lehmann's product influenced by events in China at the turn of the century, the 'Man Da Rin' sedan chair complete with seated Mandarin and concealed clockwork mechanism. Circa 1905. (See also 193, page 72.)

Colour Plate 9. The manufacturer is unknown but the fireman is a fair example of popular ladder climbing toys of the pre-World War I period with fixed key at his left shoulder. The ladder is not original but represents a reasonable replacement. Circa 1900. Fireman 19 cm high. (See also 184, page 69.)

Colour Plate 11. Probably more common than its price justifies but still an amusing toy, this 'Balky Mule' pulling a clown in a three-wheeled decorated cart was made by Lehmann, c.1912. This is a good example of this 'high survivor' toy which is also known by other names including the 'Stubborn Donkey'. 19 cm long. (See also opposite for similar example.)

213 Wearing his Lehmann trade-marked trousers, this 'Adam' porter with articulated legs pushes a porter's trolley, his clockwork mechanism concealed within the body providing motive power. Patent dates visible on border of illustrated box label. Second decade 20th century. 21 cm long. The trunk is frequently absent on such models.

*£200 — £300*

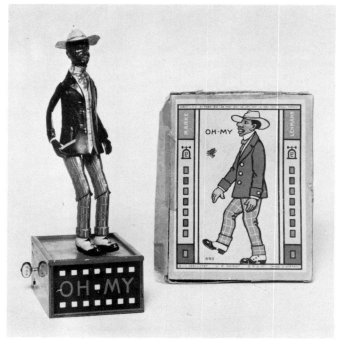

214 A Lehmann 'Oh-My' tinplate negro figure dressed in hat, jacket and checked pants, holding a baton in one hand and mounted on plinth concealing a clockwork mechanism which causes the figure to tap dance. Shown here with original box.

*£180 — £240*

215 This attractive 'Paddy and the Pig' toy by Lehmann has a clockwork mechanism concealed within the pig's saddle skirting which causes the toy to sway alarmingly. Paddy is clothed in rustic cotton attire. Second decade 20th century.

*£175 — £220*

216 This unusual musical toy comprises a mahout on a tinplate elephant appearing to operate a barrel organ with his trunk. German. Second decade 20th century. Length 23 cm.

*£70 — £90*

217 Günthermann also produced a range of tinplate and clockwork creatures; this beetle is mounted on wheels, with flapping wings and insect noise produced by mechanical bellows. Circa 1920. 19 cm long.

*£90 — £120*

218 This Günthermann tortoise has a most realistic appearance and a simple mechanism which activates head, legs and tail. Circa 1920.

*£30 — £40*

219 A simple but amusing clockwork 'Bucking Bronco' with rider by Günthermann, light tin construction. Circa 1920. 11.5 cm long.

*£40 — £60*

220 Note the presence of felt on the polisher (normally missing) to this 'Bizzy Lizzy'. Manufacturer unknown, but recent opinion suggests Fischer origin. Circa 1920. 17 cm high.

*£175 — £250*

Colour Plate 13. 'Penny Toys', simple but very collectable: a tinplate donkey standing on wheeled base, and a six-wheeled locomotive bearing initials 'J.L.H.' to cab. Hess. Circa 1920.

£30 — £40 (each)

Colour Plate 12.

Centre: The clever Lehmann miller climbing toy. 'Gustav the busy Miller' climbs to the top of the windmill and retrieves a sack of flour. 43 cm high. Examples are known in other colours. Circa 1910.

Right: A German made clockwork and tin bodied walking elephant marked 'Jumbo'. Possibly by Blomer & Schuler. Circa 1930. 9 cm high.

Foreground: A Günthermann tinplate and clockwork ladybird; circular turning with trade marks to the base. A fair example from a range of bugs and insects popular at the time. Circa 1920.

£75 — £100 (miller)
£20 — £30 (elephant)
£35 — £50 (ladybird)

The 'Balky Mule' on the left can be seen in greater detail in Colour Plate 11 on page 77.

Colour Plate 14. A product directly influenced by the popular American comic strip of the 1920s — a Toonerville Trolley. Made by H. Fischer & Co., Nuremburg, bearing copyright 1922 by Fontaine Fox, this had an ingenious clockwork mechanism with eccentric wheels with driver winding control. 13 cm long. When wound, this toy proceeds, stops and, when the driver has cranked handle, continues.

£200 — £300

221 The large head of the driver looks out of proportion. In fact it is unlikely to be original since this model is normally encountered with a smaller, moving head (see similarity to head of 214). Note the eccentric wheels producing uneven ride. Lehmann. Circa 1920.

*£120 — £150*

223 Again by Lehmann, this tinplate walking dog has articulated legs connected to a clockwork mechanism. Circa 1920. 16.5 cm long.

*£150 — £200*

222 'Quack-Quack' was the trade name for this toy by Lehmann. The imitation wicker basket with three ducklings contains a clockwork motor which provides drive to wheels and propels duck. Circa 1920. 19 cm long.

*£100 — £130*

224 Again from the popular range of animal novelty toys, this tinplate car with its monkey driver, who raises and lowers his hat, is activated by a clockwork mechanism which propels the car forward. Finished in yellow and mid-brown with floral motifs. Possibly by Distler. Circa 1920. 14.5 cm long.

*£50 — £75*

225 This tinplate clockwork horse and cart incorporates a circling and reversing motion. Greppert and Kelch. Circa 1920. 17 cm long.

*£150 — £200*

226 A Greppert and Kelch tinplate and clockwork horse drawn cart. 18 cm long. For a similar horse drawn cart by the same maker see the previous example.

*£140 — £180*

227 A German tinplate clockwork 'Jolly Clown', with flat tin head and shoulders. The opening mouth and nodding head are operated by motor. Note articulated construction. Circa 1920. 17.2 cm.

*£100 — £130*

228 Of similar construction and size to the previous example, this 'Jolly Sambo' operates in a similar way.

*£120 — £150*

229 Using a similar pressing to their earlier 'Man Da Rin' (193), Lehmann produced this clockwork toy depicting two Chinese porters carrying a box which conceals the driving mechanism. 1920s. 18 cm long.

*£80 — £120*

230 Walking the dog, this Lehmann 'Snick Snack' tinplate clockwork toy of the 1920s has a mechanism which causes the man to turn. Seen here with original box. Very scarce.

*£500 — £700*

231 A cheap 1920s tinplate clockwork cat with cord tail.

*£20 — £25*

232 A clockwork penguin. 1920s.

*£20 — £25*

233 Again from this cheap range, a tinplate clockwork bird incorporating an eccentric flywheel which generates a vibrating motion. 1920s.

*£12 — £18*

234 A pecking cockerel colourfully lithographed. Circa 1920s.

*£20 — £25*

235 A clockwork swimming seal mounted on a large driven wheel with two smaller wheels at the tail and a bell hanging from its neck. Realistically painted with black and fawn. Circa 1925. 17.8 cm.

*£30 — £40*

236 Of simple thin gauge construction, this lighthouse is powered by candle, the flame providing light for coloured windows and heat activating impeller mounted on top, which causes the entire top to revolve. Late 1920s.

*£12 — £15*

83

237 Forerunners of Action Men, these fully articulated toys have metal limbs and bodies and composition feet, hands and heads. Marked on body 'Made in Switzerland', probably by Sarba. Circa 1930. Shown here are two examples displaying articulated poses; cycle of unknown origin.

*£30 — £40 each*

238 For the musically inclined, this American made 'Zilotone' clockwork toy shows a band sergeant wielding a wooden tipped mallet. Made by Wolverine Supply and Manufacturing Co. Pittsburg, Pa., U.S.A. 1920s.

*£175 — £250*

239 Possibly aimed at the American market, this Lehmann 'Wild West Bucking Bronco' is mounted on a platform concealing a clockwork motor driving four metal wheels. These cause the bronco to buck in a realstic attempt to dislodge the cowboy. Circa 1930. 16 cm long.

*£175 — £225*

241 Bearing the trade mark CKO No 314, this amusing clockwork tinplate frog is made by Kellermann. The frog sways from side to side in his endeavours to catch a wasp-like insect. Motion is provided by cranked shaft operating in slot on leg extension, vibration provided by offset flywheel. Circa 1930. 11.5 cm high. (See also Colour Plate 15, page 89.)

*£200 — £250*

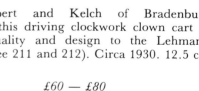

240 Greppert and Kelch of Bradenburg produced this driving clockwork clown cart of similar quality and design to the Lehmann product (see 211 and 212). Circa 1930. 12.5 cm wide.

*£60 — £80*

242 Exposing the mechanism of Kellermann's trembling frog illustrated above. The triangular offset flywheel causes trembling, and the crankshaft a swaying motion.

243 Another frog, this time a tiny German made example, having a clockwork mechanism causing a jumping motion with motor activated sprung legs. Circa 1930. 4 cm long.

*£15 — £25*

244 A Distler clockwork organ grinder — 'Jacko the Merry Organ Grinder and Monkey'. The clockwork mechanism operates small musical movement, arm and dancing monkey. Circa 1923. 17.5 cm. Note the resemblance to the Mickey Mouse organ grinder in the next example.

*£200 — £400*

245 Probably using the same pressing and organ mechanism from Distler's 'Jacko the Merry Organ Grinder' this Mickey Mouse variation shows a dancing Minnie in place of the monkey. Circa 1930. 20 cm high, 15.5 cm wide. Owing to high prices a number have been restored. (See also Colour Plate 16, page 89.)

*£400 — £800 (good condition very important)*

246 Lacking a trade mark, this Mickey Mouse toy was produced by exclusive arrangement with Ideal Films Ltd. The clockwork mechanism causes the eyes to roll and the tongue to be extended. Circa 1930. 21.5 cm high.

*£450 — £500*

247 A tinplate Mickey Mouse drummer playing a snare drum with lever at rear causing drum top to rattle against drum sticks. Stamped 'P.W.' Circa 1932. 16.5 cm high.

*£250 — £300*

248 An amusing Mickey Mouse toy entitled 'Mickey the Musical Mouse' depicting a trio, one playing violin, one playing cymbals and one dancing. When handle is turned, the heads move and a simple tune is played. Circa 1930. 24.7 cm long.

*£350 — £400*

249 Of tin and composition, this orange vendor pushes her barrow by means of clockwork activated feet. Circa 1930.

*£30 — £50*

250 This tinplate 'Man with a Suitcase' toy relies on wheels hidden under the suitcase and rotating feet. A clockwork motor is contained in the suitcase. German. Circa 1930.

*£25 — £40*

251 This clockwork crane No. 192 'Gely' has interesting four position control operating lever mechanism and is shown together with its bucket. It bears the G. Levy trade mark. German. Circa 1930. 49 cm high.

*£30 — £40*

252 A child receiving this tank may well have expected something more realistic from the artist's impression on the box! However this Marx 'Doughboy' tank has a certain charm. Circa 1930. 24 cm long. (See also Colour Plate 17, page 89.)

*£40 — £60*

253 This Louis Marx 'Ring-a-Ling' circus comprises a centrally mounted ringmaster surrounded by clockwork operated animals and clown. The lithographed circus scene base has a stop/start switch and key to side. 1930s. 19.5 cm diameter.

*£40 — £60*

254 This British made Bell Toys tinplate clockwork pig has sprung feet and flapping ears. The eccentric flywheel causes a vibrating motion exaggerated by springs in front legs.

*£20 — £30*

255 An amusing Japanese one man band made by Alps in the form of a duck playing two side drums, a base drum and cymbals; battery operated. The duck's eyes also light up when he plays. 25 cm high. Late 1940s.

*£60 — £80*

256 Although produced at a late date, this Russian made clockwork clown and balking pony is greatly influenced by the Lehmann product of pre-World War I (see Colour Plate 11, page 77, and 212, page 76). 18 cm long.

*£40 — £60*

257 A Schuco Charlie Chaplin in the guise of a cowboy, using the same pressings and mechanism as their 'Little Tramp', see next item. Circa 1930. 17 cm high.

*£80 — £100*

Colour Plate 15. A most endearing toy c.1930 is Kellermann's frog with its clever clockwork mechanism. (See also 241, page 85.)

Colour Plate 16. A very popular and attractive toy, this Mickey Mouse organ grinder displays evidence of restoration and repainting and the musical accompaniment needs attention. Good examples of this toy have fetched high prices: examine carefully and judge price accordingly since values vary by up to ten times! (See also 245, page 86.)

Colour Plate 17. There is something crude but endearing about this Marx 'Doughboy' tinplate and clockwork tank. When wound the mechanised sharpshooter appears from a hatch at the rear, aims rifle upwards and returns to sanctuary. (See also 252, page 87.)

Colour Plate 18. Three little pigs from Schuco's popular range of clockwork animals, each pig imitating the playing of a musical instrument.

£25 — £35

258 Inspired by the 'Little Tramp' this figure of Charlie Chaplin has a clockwork mechanism causing the cane to rotate. Note the original cardboard box. German. Circa 1930s. 17 cm high.

*£175 — £250*

259 Again by Schuco, this Mickey Mouse has velvet covered body with moving head. Circa 1935. 24 cm high. Visually a poor representation of Mickey.

*£50 — £70*

260 Inspired by Disney's Donald Duck, this 1930s Schuco clockwork toy has an opening beak and is part clothed. 14 cm high. The top example has an impressed Schuco name to body.

*£50 — £75*

261 From Schuco's extensive range of cloth covered clockwork creatures made in the mid-1930s are, left to right: Weight lifting mouse; a drinking mouse; a travelling pig; a chimney sweep mouse; a pig playing the flute. All 13 cm.

*£15 — £30 each*

262 Again Schuco, from the same period as the previous illustration, these large cloth covered models are, left to right: King Charles spaniel with lever operated head movements, 16 cm high, note original labels still attached; seated bulldog with lever operated moving head, 27 cm high; smaller pipe smoking bulldog with lever operated head, 20 cm high.

*£20 — £30 (spaniel and large bulldog)*
*£15 — £20 (small bulldog)*

263 These three Schuco birds are, left to right: simulated feather covered crane with spectacles, velvet covered legs, 43 cm high; owl with simulated fur covered body and lever head movements, 20 cm high; duck dressed with scarf and cap and wearing spectacles, 28 cm high.

*£15 — £25 each*

264 Two of Schuco's animal drivers, again from the 1930s. A monkey driving a three-wheeled car, 14 cm long, and a monkey wearing a top hat and carrying a balloon in similar vehicle, both clockwork.

*£15 — £18 each*

265 This Schuco clockwork toy represents a New York-to-Berlin airliner with oversized material covered pilot. Circa 1935. 9 cm long.

*£20 — £30*

Colour Plate 19. An item which bridges the field of early tinplate toys and inventive food marketing. This scarce Macfarlane Lang biscuit tin, in the form of a delivery van, has a hinged roof and turning wheels. Note the fine colour printing of driver and assistant. Circa 1920.

*£80 — £120*

Colour Plate 20. Below left: An attractive early clockwork tin fire engine bearing H.E.N. trade mark. German-made by Eberl, with elevating turntable ladder, bell and driver. Circa 1913. 22 cm long. (See also 297, page 103.)

Colour Plate 21. Though other manufacturers produced a similar garage product, this early 1920s tinplate double garage complete with clockwork limousine and open touring car is by Oro-Werke, Brandenburg, and bears their 'Orobr' trade mark. (See also 330, page 111, for illustration without drivers.)

266 A group of Schuco figures showing the versatility of their models. Left to right: bandleader, fireman with ladder, boy playing a combined drum/money box, military drummer, soldier with back pack. Circa 1935-37.

*£15 — £30 (each)*

267 A Lionel Mickey Mouse handcar No. 1100 made to operate on 0 gauge track and comprising Mickey and Minnie with articulated arms. Circa 1935.

*£150 — £200*

268 Wells was another firm to produce Disney inspired toys. Here is another handcar, this time a set complete with circular track and cardboard station buildings, shown with original box. Circa 1945. 35.5 cm wide.

*£150 — £200*

269 Of post-war manufacture, this clockwork clown and donkey was produced by Blomer and Schuler and carries their 'Jumbo' trade mark. 16 cm high. Shown with original box.

*£20 — £30*

270 An amusing and popular toy by Louis Marx, this 'Mouse Merrymakers Orchestra' comprises three musicians and a dancer, the clockwork mechanism within the piano operating all pieces. Possibly more of these models have survived than may be expected owing to adult appeal. Circa 1950.

*£250 — £350*

271 Another Disney inspired toy, a Marx 'Donald Duck Duet' showing Goofy and Donald. The clockwork operation causes Goofy to jig, and Donald to beat the drum to the accompaniment of a three-note tune. American. Circa 1950.

*£175 — £225*

272 An almost identical Marx toy, this time entitled 'Crazy Dancer' and manufactured in Great Britain. Circa 1950. 27 cm high.

*£125 — £175*

273 Using the same pressing as the previous model, Goofy appears again this time as 'The Gardener' pushing a wheelbarrow. Clockwork mechanism drives rear wheels and activates legs. Marx. Late 1940s. 21.5 cm long.

*£75 — £100*

274 By Marx, 'Charlie McCarthy' a monocled figure driving a tractor-like vehicle with oscilating motion causing bucking action. American. Circa 1950. 20 cm long. Marx also produced a jeep using the same mechanism.

*£60 — £80*

275 A crude tinplate Marx drummer boy toy consisting of a drum mounted on three-wheeled barrow. The brightly coloured figure has a mechanism which causes walking and drumming motion. American. Early 1950s. 20 cm long.

*£30 — £50*

276 A Unique Art 'Kiddy Cyclist' comprising a tinplate toddler seated on a clockwork tricycle lithographed with Disney characters. The mechanism causes the tricycle to steer and moves the child's legs. American. Circa 1950. 21.5 cm.

*£30 — £50*

# Road, Sea and Air Toys

**Models to circa 1920**

All forms of road transport are available varying from cycles to fire engines. Most of these are either clockwork or flywheel driven although some early steam driven and electric vehicles exist. Quality again is a criterion of price; on the cheaper models construction is simple with lithographed details, pressed wheels and tyres, on the more elaborate types glass windows, operating oil lamps, opening doors, rubber tyres and more complex clockwork motors are incorporated, sometimes with two speed mechanisms. (Where rubber tyres are encountered, deterioration is to be expected, perishing occurring either by hardening or softening of the rubber.) Certain models utilise three dimensional drivers or chauffeurs whilst others rely on simple pressings or lithograph work to convey realism. Products from this period are invariably from Germany though French, American and British models do exist.

Water toys comprise clockwork, some steam and even electric items. The 'Age of Steel Ships' either of shipping lines or the navies of the world, had its influence on toy manufacturers and many superb examples were produced mainly by Marklin, Bing and Carette. Submarines and 'fish' toys also found markets. Again mint or very fine examples are scarce since many will have suffered rust damage from being sailed on local ponds or pools. The large models had disappeared by the mid-twenties and gave way to more 'modern' water toys such as speedboats.

Well worth searching for are the aeronautical toys from this period — these take the form of simple heavier-than-air types, zeppelins and balloons.

*Value Point*
Box where relevant + + + +

**Post-1920 Models**

This is a fruitful period for the collector with a vast range spanning record cars, commercial and military transport, constructor kits and Tri-ang's Minic toys. The collector may wish to specialise and collect only one form of transport, and added interest will be gained by enthusiasts of real models, e.g. MG cars.

The Minic brand name introduced in the mid-thirties covered a wide range of vehicles. These were attractively painted, pre-war models having side mounted petrol cans and predominantly white tyres.

Water toys from this period are mainly civilian and include clockwork speedboats and pleasure cruisers. Hornby produced a particularly good range.

Aircraft of non-flying clockwork propulsion were produced in quantity by various makers, some with electric lights, others with sparking machine guns. However, due to their size and nature not many have survived.

Original boxes can be found and, even if mildly damaged, they enhance value.

*Value Point*
Presence of box, instructions, guarantee, etc. + + +

# Clockwork Motor Cars, Cabs, etc.

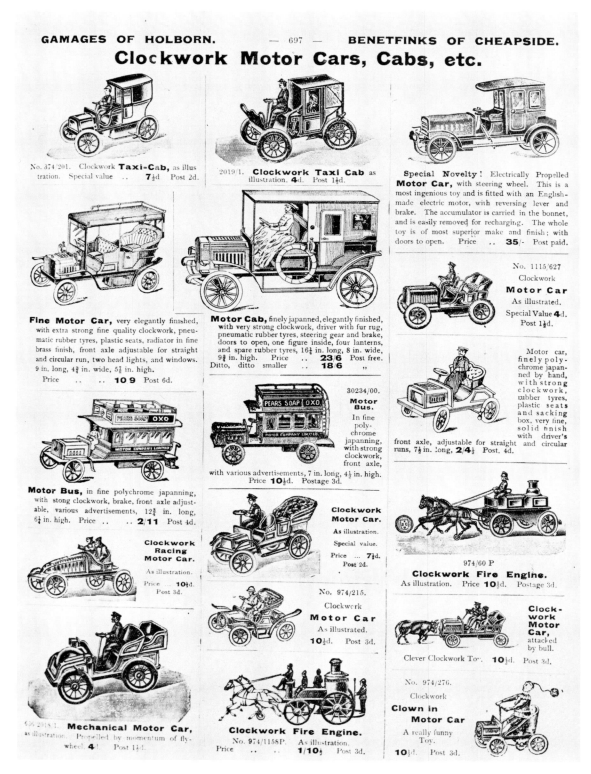

No. 374/201. Clockwork **Taxi-Cab**, as illustration. Special value .. **7½**d Post 2d.

2019/1. **Clockwork Taxi Cab** as illustration. **4**d. Post 1½d.

**Special Novelty!** Electrically Propelled **Motor Car**, with steering wheel. This is a most ingenious toy and is fitted with an English-made electric motor, with reversing lever and brake. The accumulator is carried in the bonnet, and is easily removed for recharging. The whole toy is of most superior make and finish; with doors to open. Price .. **35**/- Post paid.

**Fine Motor Car,** very elegantly finished, with extra strong fine quality clockwork, pneumatic rubber tyres, plastic seats, radiator in fine brass finish, front axle adjustable for straight and circular run, two head lights, and windows. 9 in. long, 4¾ in. wide, 5¼ in. high.
Price .. .. **10 9** Post 6d.

**Motor Cab,** finely japanned, elegantly finished, with very strong clockwork, driver with fur rug, pneumatic rubber tyres, steering gear and brake, doors to open, one figure inside, four lanterns, and spare rubber tyres, 16½ in. long, 8 in. wide, 9¾ in. high. Price .. **23/6** Post free.
Ditto, ditto smaller .. **18/6** „

No. 1115/627 Clockwork **Motor Car** As illustrated. Special Value **4**d. Post 1½d.

30234/00. **Motor Bus.** In fine polychrome japanning, with strong clockwork, front axle, with various advertisements, 7 in. long, 4½ in. high. Price **10½**d. Postage 3d.

Motor car, finely polychrome japanned by hand, with strong clockwork, rubber tyres, plastic seats and sacking box, very fine, solid finish with driver's front axle, adjustable for straight and circular runs, 7½ in. long, **2/4½** Post. 4d.

**Motor Bus,** in fine polychrome japanning, with stong clockwork, brake, front axle adjustable, various advertisements, 12¾ in. long, 6½ in. high. Price .. **2/11** Post 4d.

**Clockwork Motor Car.** As illustration. Special value. Price ... **7½**d. Post 2d.

**Clockwork Racing Motor Car.** As illustration. Price **10½**d. Post 3d.

974/60 P **Clockwork Fire Engine.** As illustration. Price **10½**d. Postage 3d.

No. 974/215. Clockwork **Motor Car** As illustrated. **10½**d. Post 3d.

**Clockwork Motor Car,** attached by bull. Clever Clockwork Toy. **10½**d. Post 3d.

No. 974/276. Clockwork **Clown in Motor Car** A really funny Toy. **10½**d. Post 3d.

**Mechanical Motor Car,** as illustration. Propelled by momentum of fly-wheel. **4**d. Post 1½d.

**Clockwork Fire Engine.** No. 974/1158P. As illustration. Price .. .. **1/10½** Post 3d.

A comprehensive range of German made tinplate vehicles on offer from 4d. (1 ½ p) to 35s. (1.75p). Gamages catalogue 1911.

# Road

277  A steam powered toy tricycle, rider missing, flywheel driving direct to rims of main wheels, finished in black and silver, fuel tray visible, crude but early. Last decade 19th century.

*£150 — £200*

278  Highly desirable this rare Bing 'Spider' steam-driven carriage has a sprung front axle, two headlamps, upholstered seats and is hand enamelled in orange and blue. Finely spoked wheels have rubber tyres. Circa 1900. 23 cm long. This example carries an early maiden and lion trade mark.

*£2,000 — £4,000*

280  Using a similar mechanism to the previous model, this Günthermann horseless carriage is finished in chocolate and yellow with gilded details. Again rubber tyres are used. Similar horseless carriages were illustrated in Gamages 1911 catalogue, this time with side mounted winder, see page 97, top centre. Circa 1905.

*£150 — £200*

279  An interesting rear key-wound open car by Günthermann, having imitation wickerwork body and folded hood, finished in green with red interior. Wheels with rubber tyres. Circa 1905. 14 cm long.

*£150 — £200*

## MODEL STEAM FIRE ENGINE.

The above Steam Fire Engine is from a design by Mr. W. J. Bassett-Lowke, and is a vast improvement upon the usual obsolete types on the market. It is fitted with a powerful Double-action Slide Valve Cylinder, with exhaust into Chimney; solid Turned Fly-wheel, powerful Pump, with Air Chamber and two Deliveries. The Boiler is tubular, made of brass, and highly polished, and is fitted with large size Spirit Lamp.

The Engine is mounted on a proper designed Carriage with shafts, the Wheels are cast iron, with nickel-plated rims and imitation springs, Suction Pipe and Rose, also delivery Pipes and Branches are sent out with the Model. This is certainly one of the most novel productions and is sure to give every satisfaction. 12in. long without shafts, 5in. wide, 8in. high Price **£2 2s. 0d.**

++++++++++++

### Novel Model Steam Engines.

*The Model Engineer and Electrician,* January 7th, 1904, says :—

"Two very good miniature steam engines have been received from Messrs. Bassett-Lowke & Co., 20, Kingswell street, Northampton—one a model steam turbine and the other a model fire engine. Both are of excellent finish, and work extremely well. The turbine, which we tested, runs at a rate of 30,000 revs. per minute with a moderate pressure of 20lbs., and is remarkable for its perfect balance at this speed. The fire engine is a very realistic model, well-made, and works splendidly. It has two jets and a by-pass; the suction hose is fitted with a strainer, and the delivery side of the pump has an efficient air-chamber. The small jet will throw a very fine stream for a distance of some 3ft., and the other one a larger stream double this distance. This jet delivers—to use a model measure of capacity—a teacupful of water per minute continuously, and whilst the engine is working, the steady thump, thump, thump, common to the prototype, is present in the model—of course, in a proportionate degree."

282 A desirable Carette clockwork open four-seater tourer bearing the number '50' on its radiator, and finished in scarlet with cream and gilt lining. It has simulated padded seats and glass windscreen. Circa 1905. 21.5 cm long. (For a similar example but having roof and passengers see *The Golden Age of Toys*, page 185.)

*£450 — £600*

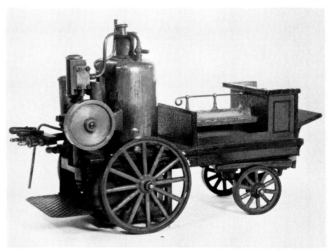

281 Illustrated in Bassett-Lowke's 1905-6 catalogue (see left), this extremely scarce and desirable Bing steam horse-drawn fire engine was advertised at 2 gns. (£2.10). Having single oscillating cylinder, vertical brass boiler finished in original red and yellow with black lining, complete but for shaft, front handrail, hoses, etc. 32 cm long.

*£1,500 — £2,000*

283 The wheels on this clockwork fire engine indicate probable manufacture by Günthermann. Finished in scarlet with black details and gilded brightwork, two firemen are missing. The mechanism causes a bell mounted underneath to be rung by the front axle at intervals. First decade 20th century. 20 cm long.

*£150 — £200*

284 Steam powered, this scarce Doll and Co. open touring car is spirit fired, the bonnet opening to reveal the boiler. Rubber tyred artillery type wheels with side mounted spare, three opening doors, operating clutch and steering; finished in maroon and black.

*£800 — £1,200*

286 By Lehmann this clockwork delivery van, painted in green and gold with red side drapes, is complete with driver. Circa 1910. 18 cm long.

*£200 — £250*

285 Flywheel operated, this Hessmobil car is finished in scarlet with black and gilt details and simulated padded seats. The Hess trade mark is visible on the side. Proportionally unattractive; the chauffeur lacks legs. Circa 1910. 23 cm long.

*£200 — £300*

287 A clockwork tram-car of French origin with staircases front and rear, finished in cream with scarlet lining. Circa 1905. 28 cm long.

*£175 — £250*

288 Attractively enamelled, but distressed, this French open touring car retains some of the well-detailed fittings of the period, realistic horn and side lamp. It is rubber tyred and has a porcelain chauffeur which is probably not original. Clockwork mechanism. Circa 1910. 35 cm long.

*£150 — £200*

289 A Bing clockwork limousine retaining original scarlet finish with black roof, chauffeur, side lamps, door handles, etc. Side mounted lever operated brake, trade mark at rear. Circa 1914. 31 cm long.

*£350 — £550*

290 Again by Bing, this clockwork open tourer has a similar chassis to the previous model and is finished in scarlet with cherry red and yellow lining. Note the driver is of composition and possibly not original. Circa 1914.

*£200 — £300*

291 This fine later Edwardian clockwork limousine is an example from the Carette range. Note attention to detail in the form of lamps, door handles, etc. Tinplate tyres, lever operated brake, uniformed chauffeur. Finished in dark green with red details, lined in black and gilt. Circa 1910. 40 cm long.

*£900 — £1,200*

292 A popular and much sought-after model, this Bing open two-seater Mercedes retains its original dark green finish lined in yellow with pink upholstery, rubber tyred artillery type wheels and lever operated clockwork mechanism. Circa 1912. 24 cm long.

*£600 — £800*

293 Lacking any mechanism, this push-along open tourer by Brimtoy is finished in a translucent scarlet with black and gold lining. Spoked wheels. Circa 1914. 28 cm long.

*£140 — £180*

294 A pre-World War I push-along German tourer, driver, mudguard and hood missing. Finished in cream and blue. 14.5 cm.

*£50 — £80*

295 A crisp example of a pre-World War I clockwork landaulette by Karl Bub or Carette. The model has simple steering, a hand brake and opening rear doors. Note the method by which the mudguards are supported. Maroon and black. 28 cm long. Very similar to the next item.

*£400 — £500*

296 A similar item to the previous Bub or Carette landaulette. Note the tyre colour difference, though paintwork the same. 24 cm long. This model is also known to exist painted as an ambulance.

*£400 — £500*

297 An early (pre-World War I) clockwork fire engine by Hans Eberl, having elevating and extending turntable ladder, bell and driver. H.E.N. trade mark. Attractive simplicity. Circa 1913. 22 cm overall. (See also Colour Plate 20, page 92.)

*£125 — £175*

298 A Bing pre-World War I tinplate and clockwork limousine, the clockwork mechanism driving the back axle. Finished in maroon and buff with orange, black and yellow trim, complete with uniformed chauffeur, opening rear doors and hand brake, etc., side lamps missing. 31 cm long.

*£350 — £450*

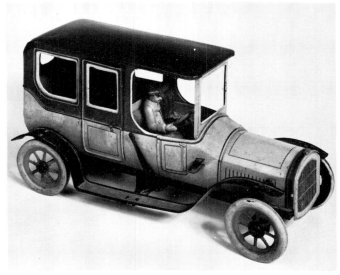

299 An early 20th century American heavy gauge tinplate flywheel drive car of crude form, complete with driver. Finished in original red paintwork. Note six wheels. 30.5 cm long.

*£150 — £250*

300 Probably from the same manufacturer, another flywheel driven toy. This van retains much original blue paint finish and is lined in gold.

*£100 — £150*

301 Note the clear Lehmann trade mark to the side of this 'AHA' clockwork delivery van with recessed roof rack. Finished in red with green lined wheels, this particular example had a tie-on label marked 4¾ d. (fourpence three farthings). Circa 1910.

*£125 — £200*

302 This Lehmann 'Echo' clockwork motorcyclist is pulley driven; note the small supporting wheels. Variations exist. Circa 1912. 21.5 cm long.

*£350 — £500*

303 German made, this taxi by H. Fischer of Nuremberg has an interesting feature — a folding canopy. It has three hinged side doors, meter and hire sign to nearside. Opera lamps, headlamp and klaxon missing. Coil mainspring.

*£400 — £500*

304 Shown with its bonnet open and revealing a 6-cylinder engine, this Moko clockwork saloon has side mounted lever engaging forward/neutral/reverse gears. Finished in green and black, with chauffeur. Note Semperit Cord 31 x 4 tyres. Circa 1920. 24 cm long.

*£150 — £200*

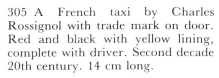

305 A French taxi by Charles Rossignol with trade mark on door. Red and black with yellow lining, complete with driver. Second decade 20th century. 14 cm long.

*£125 — £175*

307 Lehmann produced a vast variety of cheap clockwork toys which are attractive to collectors. This clockwork 'Also' car shows Lehmann's distinctive key design, a yellow body with red bordering and liveried driver. 10 cm long.

*£100 — £150*

306 Another scarce steam model is a Bing steam roller dating from the second decade of the 20th century. It is fitted with simple oscillating cylinder, solid flywheel and this example is finished in good original black livery, lined orange and yellow. 26 cm long.

*£450 — £600*

308 This push-along Brimtoy tinplate taxi is finished in translucent blue with gilt lining. Circa 1920. 27 cm long. It is marked 'Brimtoy Brand British Make'.

*£140 — £180*

309 Here shown without its upper deck, this Günthermann clockwork bus is starting handle wound, with crown wheel drive to back axle; part of the wire spring type clockwork motor is visible underneath. This example retains its driver and headlamps and is finished in scarlet with black and yellow lining and details. Circa 1920. 28 cm long.

*£150 — £200*
*£300 — £500 (complete)*

310 A Günthermann clockwork tram-car finished in scarlet with yellow lining and black details. Axle, activated bell, glass windows, staircases at either end and complete with driver. Circa 1920. 25.5 cm long.

*£300 — £400*

311 Günthermann again. A double-decked tram finished in red with yellow and black lining and having a hinged pick up arm, glazed windows and a clockwork mechanism powering rear wheels. Circa 1920s. 24 cm long.

*£180 — £250*

312 Finished in navy blue with yellow lining, grey interior and red seats this Bing open car has lever operated brake, glass windscreen, etc. Note side mounted lamps are missing.

*£350 — £450*

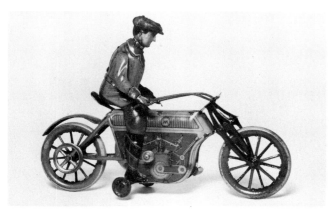

313 Flywheel driven, this motorcycle and rider are attractively lithographed. The flywheel motor drives near wheel by belt drive as did real motorcycles of this period. 'WK' trade mark. Second decade 20th century. 21 cm long.

*£200 — £300*

314 By Orobr this clockwork fire pump is attractively finished in grey with scarlet and brass coloured trim. Simple steering. Second decade 20th century. 16.5 cm long.

*£175 — £250*

317 Another Hess tourer this time showing detail of upholstery, activating handle and pressed spoked wheels. The previous Hess tourer has voided wheels, otherwise they are very similar.

*£200 — £250*

319 By Whitley Tansley & Co., this clockwork tinplate tourer comes complete with driver. The company was one of the small tinplate toy manufacturers which produced an excellent clockwork model of the World War I British tank 'Barney' (see next illustration).

*£100 — £150*

315 This French tram-car by Rossignol is finished in green and cream with orange trim. Roof mounted cable conductor. Circa 1920. 21 cm long.

*£150 — £200*

316 An open clockwork tourer by Hess which has a flywheel driven mechanism operated by imitation starting handle. Finished in scarlet with black and yellow lining, complete with driver. 1920s. 27 cm long.

*£200 — £250*

318 Again by Hess, this flywheel driven landaulette is finished in original dark green with black and white lining, orange window frames, complete with driver. Circa 1920s. 21 cm long.

*£200 — £250*

320 Shown in mock battlefield, this 'Whitanco' clockwork 'Barney' tank has realistic tracks with tensioning adjustment, rivet detail, etc. Fake gun barrels, opening rear hatch enabling inspection of motor. Painted in 'mud' brown.

*£50 — £80*

321 From the twenties, this fine Bing limousine is powered by a 2-speed clockwork motor and brake lever, the activating levers visible by the driver's door. Opening rear doors, scuttle mounted side lamps, chauffeur. Finished in cherry red and black, lined yellow. 38.8 cm long.

*£500 — £700*

322 A similar limousine, this time showing glass windscreen in open position and front bumper which was sometimes fitted to this model. A cheap version exists without rubber tyres, spare wheel, opening windscreen or 2-speed mechanism.

*£500 — £700*

323 This is the less expensive version of the Bing limousine having pressed tin tyres, no opening windscreen, sidelights or spare wheel. Nor is it fitted with a brake or 2-speed mechanism. Finished in black and olive green with white lining. 38 cm long.

*£350 — £450*

 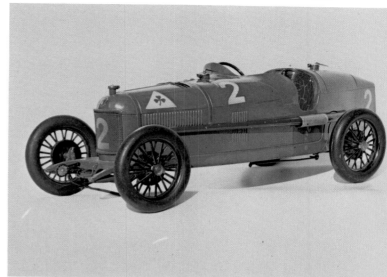

Colour Plate 22. These C.I.J. P2 Alfa Romeos were produced in the national colours of countries competing in Grand Prix racing, hence silver represents Germany, blue France, red Italy, and green Great Britain. These large size clockwork cars were classic toys from a Golden Age in motor racing. The silver produced in 1929, the blue 1926. (See also 336, 337 and 338, page 114.)

Colour Plate 23. One of the finest tinplate toys ever produced is this J.E.P. French made clockwork Hispano Suisa touring car with sprung front bumper, electric lights, gear box, operating steering, treaded tyres and windscreen. A Rolls Royce version was also produced and one is more likely to encounter this type in the British Isles. Other colours available. Circa 1928. 52 cm long. (See also 339, page 115.)

Colour Plate 24. Produced by Citroën in 1923, this 5 cv tourer is a very realistic model and captures the charm of the full size vehicle made by Citroën. Clockwork mechanism operating steering; windscreen missing. Circa 1928. (See also 340, page 115.)

324 Once again by Bing but at the cheaper end of their range, this Model T Ford 2-door coupé has obvious charm. Light gauge tinplate with clockwork mechanism. Painted black — the colour of the day for Fords. The trade mark appears on number plate. 1920s. 16 cm long.

*£175 — £250*

325 Note 'Bing' printed to lower nearside corner of radiator on this clockwork limousine. Complete with driver it is painted in orange and black, trade mark to rear. Circa 1920s. 19 cm long.

*£175 — £250*

326 A well-made World War I type clockwork tank of non-commercial manufacture, having powerful clockwork mechanism. The release of pressure on a screw at the rear regulates the speed. Circa 1920. 29 cm long.

*£30 — £40*

327 A Doll et Cie spirit-fired live steam road roller having single cylinder mechanism driving flywheel with coiled wire drive to nearside roller. Finished in black with red trim and polished brass boiler. Circa 1925. 21.5 cm.

*£175 — £250*

328 By the same maker, this oil pump wagon is finished in scarlet with black wheels, and has operating pumps and opening end revealing glass container. Circa 1920. 16.5 cm.

*£75 — £125*

329 Interesting owing to its mechanism, this Eberl clockwork car complete with driver is not only driven forward but is caused to roll over. Note external supports. Circa 1925. 24.5 cm long.

*£125 — £175*

330 A 1920s double garage by Orobr complete with its two cars (without drivers), one being a yellow and black clockwork limousine, 14 cm long, the other an open touring car in green and black, 16 cm long. (See also Colour Plate 21, page 92 for illustration with drivers.)

*£200 — £250*

331 This Tipp & Co. clockwork fire pump is an attractive toy and is unusual in that all the original figures are present. Note the simulated Dunlop Cord tyres and bell. 1920s and '30s.

*£100 — £150*

Colour Plate 25. *Kaye-Dons Silver Bullet land speed racing car made by Günthermann, advertised in Gamages October 1930 catalogue as being available (as shown) in pressed steel at 8s.11d. (44½p), or in super quality chromium plate at 16s.6d. (82½p) which must now be very scarce. (See also 342, page 115.)*

Colour Plate 26. *Meccano No. 2 constructor car, shown with some of its accessories and instruction sheet. (See also 371, page 125.)*

Colour Plate 27. *A scarce Tri-ang 'Magic Midget' MG record car, having powerful clockwork motor, rubber wheels with polished aluminium discs, complete with driver. Some dents, paint chipped and rust evident. Circa 1935. 40 cm long. (See also 374, page 126.)*

Colour Plate 28. *From Tri-ang's Minic post-war clockwork and tinplate range of 'scale model' vehicles, a cable trailer and its original box, and a Minic Transport delivery lorry. Circa 1948.*

£10 — £15 (trailer)
£8 — £12 (lorry)

Colour Plate 29. *An immediate post-war clockwork Minic jeep was available in two sizes, No. 1 (small) and No. 2 (large). Well detailed copies of originals. No. 2 box shown. Tri-ang also produced a pedal jeep, a pedal powered version on this popular theme. (See also 391, page 130.)*

£10 — £15 (No. 1)
£12 — £18 (No. 2)

332 Another Tipp & Co. clockwork fire engine, this time with fire escape. Note how the same body is used in this and the previous example. Again complete with four firemen and bell.

*£120 — £180*

333 An attractive clockwork fire engine by Distler, this one with ladder, though the upper section is missing. This body pressing was used in more than one application which explains the slots for additional firemen.

*£100 — £150*

334 A Lines Bros. Tri-ang large scale 'Royal Mail' push-along van of wood and metal construction, rubber tyres. There is some restoration. 1920s.

*£50 — £75*

335 A selection of pressed tinplate and lithographed stand-up representations of locomotives and an aeroplane of the very attractive 'give-away' type presented by *Modern Boy* and other comics in the late 1920s. Approx. 13 cm long.

*£1.50 — £3 (each)*

336 A rear view of the legendary P2 Alfa Romeo produced by C.I.J. Note this model has treaded tyres and lacks brake drums and shock absorbers in design. Shown here with original box — the original price being 35s. (£1.75). Circa 1929. (See also Colour Plate 22, page 109.)

*£500 — £700*

337 Another earlier example of the P2 Alfa Romeo. Note presence of André dampers, brake drums and smooth tyres as indicated on the label on original box. This model is c.1926. (See also Colour Plate 22, page 109.)

*£500 — £700*

338 The two previous P2s.

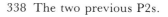

339 A road view of the Hispano Suisa, shown in Colour Plate 23 on page 109, illustrating transmission, steering, sprung bumper, etc., and also displaying some restoration to running board and bumper guard.

*£800 — £1,200*

340 An underview of the Citroën 5cv Clover Leaf tourer, seen in Colour Plate 24 on page 109, showing simplicity of the mechanism, steering and brake; the mainspring is missing. Note André Citroën's trade mark.

*£350 — £450*

341 From the Kingsbury company (U.S.A.), this model of Malcolm Campbell's Bluebird record car came with cunningly hidden key. The company was responsible for making other record cars including The Golden Arrow and the 1000 h.p. Sunbeam. Late 1920s.

*£150 — £250*

343 Also Günthermann, this time a successful car — the original exists in the National Motor Museum, Beaulieu. The Golden Arrow uses a similar clockwork mechanism to the previous model. Circa 1929. 54.5 cm long.

*£125 — £175*

342 A tinplate model of a contender for the world land speed record in the 1930s, and scarcer than other similar toys in that the original car was unsuccessful. Made by Günthermann (unmarked, except 'foreign') with clockwork motor handbrake, applied flags and pressed wheels and tyres. 56 cm long. (See also Colour Plate 25, page 112.)

*£180 — £220*

344 Of unknown manufacture, this limousine has electric lights and opening doors. The near mudguard is missing and the whole effect proportionally unattractive. Circa 1930.

*£130 — £180*

345 A clockwork double-decker open top bus by Bing, having external staircase and canopy to driving compartment. Nicely lithographed with destination boards, advertisements, etc. 1920s. 19 cm long.

*£225 — £300*

346 This slightly later double-decker bus is by Distler. Although the upper deck is covered there is an external staircase. Lithographed destination boards, advertisements, etc. Circa 1930. 22 cm long.

*£350 — £500*

347 A French single-decker bus by Rossignol finished in green and cream. Open driving compartment with canopy. Circa 1930. 20 cm long. This type of bus was used in Paris until the 1960s.

*£200 — £300*

348 An unattractive toy which reflects the utility and futuristic ideals of the 1930s, this clockwork ambulance by Marx has a hinged rear door. 36 cm long.

*£50 — £80*

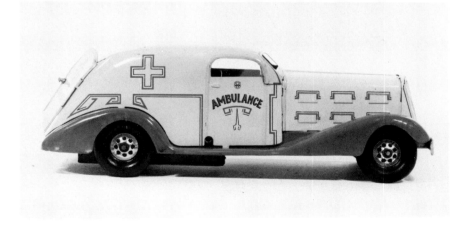

349 Two views of a mint example of a Günthermann roll-back roof coupé, having electric lights, opening passenger door, trunk. Finished in blue with orange lining and mudguards, but also known finished in orange. Circa 1930.

*£400 — £600*

350 A smaller version of the Günthermann roll-back roofed saloon, finished in mustard yellow with ochre running boards. Circa 1930. 37 cm.

*£350 — £450*

351 Unmistakably Renault by bonnet design, this J.E.P. clockwork saloon is well appointed having spotlight, klaxon, headlamps, etc. Motor wound from front, driving propeller shaft to near wheels. Finished in olive green with black and gilt. Circa 1930. 34 cm long. Toys bearing close resemblance to actual cars, have wider appeal

*£350 — £500*

352 Another J.E.P. tinplate saloon, this time a Delage shown here with its original box. This model makes use of the same chassis and body as the previous model, but substitutes a Delage radiator, bonnet, etc. Finished in maroon with grey, black and scarlet details. Circa 1930.

*£450 — £600*

353 Using a similar chassis to previous J.E.P. models, this Voisin tourer has operating gear lever, head-lamps, klaxon, etc., and is finished in blue with navy lining. Late 1920s.

*£350 — £400*

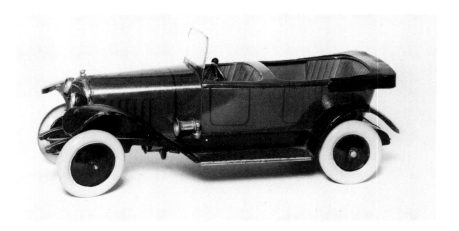

354 Of American origin, this touring car has a clockwork motor and tinplate driver. Finished in scarlet with silver and green trim. Rear wheels stamped 'pat Nov 1-2 USA'. Circa 1930. 32 cm long.

*£50 — £75*

355 Of very light construction, this attractive Wells tinplate clockwork lorry bears lithographs finished in red and green with gilded letters. Note 'play-worn' appearance. Circa 1930. 16.5 cm long.

*£75 — £100*

356 A very sound example of the same Wells 'BP' lorry but lacking clockwork mechanism. Collectors will no doubt have their personal views concerning lack of motor, but its absence in this case is not as crucial as one where the toy's charm relies on mechanisation.

*£100 — £125*

357 An unusual motorcycle and sidecar combination finished in red with lithographed details and uniformed crew. German. Circa 1930. 23 cm long.

*£100 — £140*

358 Structo produced this interesting, robustly constructed, clockwork gear driven model. The view without body shows the three main springs working steering, handbrake, gearbox and crown wheel and pinion. Nut and bolt construction two-seater coupé body with rear mounted spare wheel. Appeared in orange and blue, though other colours may exist. Black chassis. Close examination of gears is advised as powerful clockwork motor can strip teeth.

*£175 — £250*

359 'Structo toys make men of boys' was included on the transferred trade mark on the radiator of this model, which has a clockwork mechanism and cast artillery type wheels with 'clincher' rubber tyres. The body has been crudely repainted. 31 cm long.

*£75 — £125*

360 Possibly by Burnett, this car came as a kit for assembly by a child. Clockwork, of simple construction, finished in cream, blue and black. Circa 1930s.

*£75 — £100*

361 A Carter Paterson carrier van by Wells, now lacking its driver and clockwork mechanism. Finished in olive green with black and scarlet details and lettering to sides. Circa 1935. 11.5 cm.

*£80 — £120*

362 A 'Primus Motor Chassis' constructor toy by W. Butcher, London, finished in original green and silver paintwork. Radiator top and mounted AA badge. Circa 1930. 33 cm long.

*£100 — £150*

*Colour Plate 30. Marklin were big producers of tinplate battleships. This is one of their range of British ships, the H.M.S. Edward VII, a clockwork model mounted on its stand. Note the ram prow reminiscent of early ironclad ships. This model was sold by Sotheby's Belgravia in May 1980 for £4,500. Circa 1905. 52 cm long.*

*Colour Plate 31. This illustration shows the fine Marklin battleship Weissenberg, which was sold in New York by PB Eighty-Four in December 1979 for $21,000. The description included: "four lifeboats on davits, anchor and winch, the bow with cast decoration, bridge, cannons and gun turrets, twin funnels and twin masts surmounted by star-spangled banners, the rudder adjusted by an eight-pointed ship's wheel above, the clockwork mechanism concealed within, operating a four-bladed propeller at the rear. Finished in hand painted grey with porthole detail and white-painted handrails, complete with key and black painted wheeled support." There has been some minor repainting, and the bow light is an addition. Circa 1905. 87.6 cm long.*

363 Another French clockwork Paris bus by Charles Rossignol having lithographed destination boards finished in green and cream with yellow lining. 30.5 cm long.

*£120 — £180*

364 A scarce International Stores biscuit tin in the form of an articulated delivery van, having a hinged roof finished in light and dark brown, with gold coloured lettering and registration plate 'IS 1932'. Circa 1930. 32 cm overall.

*£100 — £150*

365 A pre-war Wells and Co. tinplate and clockwork 'GR Royal Mail' van, finished in red with black roof and yellow detail, lithographed driver. Note the clarity of the Wells trade mark on driver's door. Circa 1935. 17 cm long.

*£50 — £70*

366 Advertised (at 35s.!) in *The Meccano Magazine* of 1931, this 'Ranlite' (bakelite) Singer saloon with sliding roof and sprung bumpers was manufactured by Automobiles (Geographical) Ltd. of Halifax, Yorks. An Austin and a Golden Arrow record car were also available in the same material.

*£150 — £200*

367 Available in 1932 at 10s.6d., this Tri-ang six-wheeled tipping transport truck had a momentum flywheel motor and balloon tyres, missing from the example shown. Also supplied with a load of six boxes. 51 cm long.

£20 — £30

368 Also 10s.6d. when first available, this Tri-ang Magic sports car although without headlights, radiator, a tyre and seat back is still an interesting and collectable toy. Made in heavy gauge tinplate and also available at a reduced price without spare wheel, lights, etc.

£30 — £50

369 This Mercedes tourer by Tipp & Co. was called 'Der Wagon des Fuhrer'. Attention to detail in the form of lamps, horns, etc., though the side mounted spare wheels are missing. Finished in dark blue with silver lining. Mid- to late 1930s. 23 cm long.

£275 — £350

370 This Citroën car chassis with detachable rubber-tyred wheels, lifting bonnet, headlamps, working steering, etc., is finished in black with chrome trim. Mid-1930s. 38 cm long.

£200 — £275

Colour Plate 32. Shown here, a complete no. 22 set of Modelled Miniatures displaying how attractive the colourful painted finish made these models, with original Modelled Miniatures box — after April 1934 these models were re-named Dinky Toys. (See the announcement in 'The Meccano Magazine', December 1933, page 144, and items 467-472.)

£1,200 — £1,600 (boxed set)

Colour Plate 33. A Dinky 28 series van advertising Dunlop tyres. Note evidence of metal fatigue. (See also 478, page 160.)

371 During the thirties Meccano introduced two constructor car kits. Illustrated here is an example of a No. 2 kit which displays electric lights (available as an extra). Bodies, mudguards and radiators were interchangeable on a common chassis with short or long wheelbase options. Such models are scarce with original windscreen. 33 cm long with pointed tail and long wheelbase extension. (See also Colour Plate 26, page 112.)

*£175 - £250*

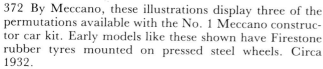

372 By Meccano, these illustrations display three of the permutations available with the No. 1 Meccano constructor car kit. Early models like these shown have Firestone rubber tyres mounted on pressed steel wheels. Circa 1932.

*£100 — £150*

373 A good example of a Meccano non-constructor sports car, this model typifies sports cars of the 1930s and is much scarcer than Meccano constructor cars. The model has simple steering mechanism, the exhaust pipe doubles as brake and the windscreen has Perspex. Circa 1935.

*£150 — £200*

374 An impressive toy, this Tri-ang MG 'Magic Midget' possessed a powerful clockwork motor. The wheels are solid rubber with polished aluminium discs. The box shows George Eyston's photograph and facsimile signature. This model has increased appeal as many MG followers would also be keen to possess such a piece. Cost price in 1935 10s.6d. 40 cm long. (See also Colour Plate 27, page 112.)

*£125 — £175*

375 Typical of the Marx 1930s range comes this creeper tractor, which possesses an uncanny ability to climb over obstacles, books, etc. Though of crude appearance it has a certain charm and is shown here with its box.

*£20 — £30*

376 A Marx clockwork American fire engine having battery operated lights, clockwork mechanism incorporating siren, hose; the ladders are missing. Heavy gauge tinplate body. Circa 1939. 36 cm long.

*£50 — £75*

378 A pre-World War II Schuco clockwork motorcyclist with automatic direction changer. Note the ring ticket with 'Germanic' numerals attached to handlebars.

*£40 — £60*

377 Three German pre-World War II clockwork motorcyclists including one by Kellermann with pillion passenger half missing. Complete, he would have turned with the cornering of the machine.

*£50 — £75 (each)*

379 From the mid-thirties this Schuco-Lizenz 12-cylinder Auto-Union clockwork racing car has automatic steering. Painted silver. 10 cm long.

*£20 — £30*

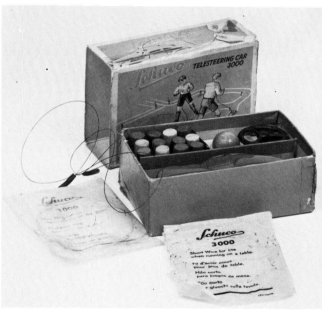

381 A pre-war Schuco 'Telesteering Car 3000', here shown complete with its box, obstacles, control cables, steering wheel, etc.

*£20 — £30*

380 Left: By Schuco, the sports car owes much to the BMW 328 in appearance. It has two clockwork motors, one operating a klaxon-like horn, the other to propel it along. Fitted with handbrake and working steering. Centre: Based on the Mercedes 125 racing car this Schuco product has detachable wheels with knock off hub caps and was sold complete with tool kit. It has rack and pinion steering and differential, both visible from underneath, and also employs an unusual keyless winder. A fascinating toy! Produced pre- and post-war. Right: Another Schuco product using the same body as the sports car. This model is intriguing in that German ingenuity surpasses itself by having four forward speeds, and one reverse, controlled by governor. A finger-operated clutch is on the nearside of its body; handbrake is also incorporated. Mainly produced pre-war.

*£30 — £50 (left)*
*£25 — £40 (centre)*
*£35 — £50 (right)*

382 Two examples of a Schuco studio GP Mercedes racing car available in various colours. The steering wheel is missing on one illustration, as is often the case with die-cast added parts, rubber wheels and chrome exhausts. Introduced about 1936. 15 cm long.

*£25 — £40*
*£15 — £25 (without steering wheel)*

383 This Ford Y type saloon by Minic has white tyres and the tell-tale petrol can, both of which indicate pre-war manufacture. The box (£100 Ford Saloon), of course, confirms this.

*£35 — £50*

384 Another Minic Ford, this time a light van available in other colours. Post-war this model was produced with plastic wheels and without petrol can. Note the hole in the box which enabled its colour to be determined without removal.

*£35 — £50*

385 A pre-war Minic clockwork breakdown lorry having two motors, the second to activate the crane. Note the running board mounted petrol can and white tyres.

*£30 — £50*

386 Historically interesting in view of Edward VIII's short reign, this 'ER Royal Mail' van by Minic is not as scarce as might be thought. A good pre-war example, with tyres not perished.

*£30 — £40*

387 Left: The scarce pre-war Minic Daimler tourer. Variations on this model include some with electric lights, sliding roof, etc. Right: The Minic limousine had a relatively short production life; possibly a model of a Humber. Pre-war.

*£30 — £50 (tourer standard)*
*£60 — £100 (tourer de luxe)*
*£20 — £30 (limousine)*

388 Three examples of pre-war Minic passenger vehicles include the four-seater tourer, the fastback coupé and the learner driver car — the L-plate is just visible on the radiator on the right hand car.

*£20 — £30 (left)*
*£20 — £30 (centre)*
*£30 — £40 (right)*

389 Pre-war Minic produced a construction set of six vehicles. Shown here a selection of parts including petrol cans, transfer sheets and catalogues, and three bodies for delivery van, limousine and open truck.

*£50 — £80 (as shown)*

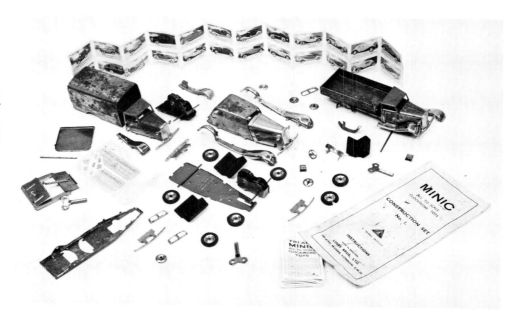

390 A selection from Tri-ang's range of pre- and post-war Minic vehicles. Left: The post-war steam roller with plastic roller (pre-war had a wooden roller) has a clockwork mechanism which causes the vehicle to oscillate forward and backward. Centre: The post-war tractor shown with its box; here again wooden wheels would indicate pre-war manufacture as would white rubber creeper tracks. Lower right: A pre-war Minic tank, this time showing wooden wheels. Unfortunately the white rubber tracks have perished and are missing; the turret rotates. Top right: This model of a post-war fire engine should have a two-piece extending ladder and a bell; also produced pre-war as a de luxe version with electric lights.

£8 — £15 (each)

392 Heavy timber haulage represented here by Minic, this articulated mechanical horse and load again appeared with wheel variations. Early models had pressed tin, later productions die-cast, and final productions plastic.

£10 — £15

391 Announced shortly after the cessation of hostilities, the Minic clockwork jeep became a popular toy. Issued for some time, it appeared in various shades of green from olive drab to deep bronze gloss. Different transfers may also be encountered, and later models appear with smooth rubber tyres. The model shown (No. 1), has plastic wheels. (See also Colour Plate 29, page 112.)

£10 — £15

393 Again by Minic, this dustcart is an attractive model having six sliding plated hatches, plated tinplate wheels. It is available in various colours.

£10 — £15

394 Difficult to find from the post-war range, this Southern Railway delivery van has opening rear doors painted in 'Southern' green and bears an interesting Penguin advertisement (Penguin being a subsidiary trade name of Tri-ang).

*£20 — £30*

395 One of the last of the clockwork models by Minic was the forward control series of articulated vehicles. Shown here is the petrol tanker version with green cab, and red tanker with gold and black lettering. Note the plastic wheels. Minic abandoned clockwork and produced some of the late models of its range with push-and-go mechanisms.

*£10 — £15*

396 The Vauxhall shown here was one of the Minic body styles available. It is interesting to note that these models used wooden seats throughout the production period.

*£10 — £15*

397 Shown here with its original box, this clockwork post-war Minic London Transport bus carries a Bovril advertisement.

*£25 — £40*

398 Although widely used during the war, staff cars have not been produced by many makers. This camouflaged clockwork example is by Mettoy and comes complete with driver. Accurate period detail includes position of numbers and white bumpers. 35 cm overall.

*£35 — £50*

399 Large and impressive, this Mettoy racing car was produced in the late 1940s/early 1950s. It is reminiscent of the Indianapolis cars of the period in its litho work; finished in blue and yellow.

*£60 — £80*

400 A post-war Chad Valley U-Builda tourer, again very simple construction, with clockwork mechanism and rear-mounted spare wheel. Becoming scarce. Circa 1948.

*£40 — £60*

401 From the immediate post-war period, this cheap and crudely made tinplate coupé had a lever-operated brake and came in red or blue. Usually the wings, radiator and wheels were lightly plated. British. Late 1940s.

*£12 — £20*

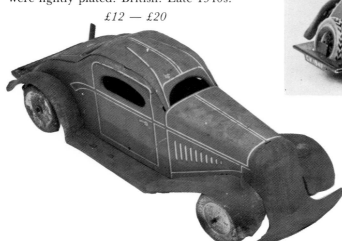

402 Post-war constructional saloon car by Chad Valley. Note the number plate 'CV 1947'. Finished in red with black mudguards. 24.5 cm long.

*£50 — £75*

403 This Carr's biscuit tin in the form of a London Transport double-decker bus was produced by Chad Valley and carries both Carr's and Chad Valley advertisements to the sides. The model illustrated has a clockwork mechanism and was the only type of clockwork biscuit tin ever manufactured, although it was also produced by Carr's without the clockwork mechanism. Finished in orange and red. Circa 1947. 25 cm long.

*£100 — £150*

404 By Chad Valley, this clockwork saloon was produced shortly after the war in blue with black mudguards, chassis, etc. Note the cheap lithographed windows depicting passengers. Circa 1948.

*£40 — £60*

405 Two views of an Arnold clockwork motorcycle and rider. When wound the mechanism causes the rider to mount motorcycle, drive off, dismount and repeat. Stop start control on side. Circa 1950.

*£100 — £150*

406 Modelled on the early Porsche, this super-streamlined German model has electric lights, steering and clockwork motor operated by the driver's door handle. Finished in metallic silver blue. Post-war.

*£25 — £40*

407 Realistically constructed, this Russian-made AM tinplate lorry has operating crane, opening doors, etc., and is shown here with original box. 1950s. 40 cm long.

*£30 — £50*

408 A selection of cheaper tinplate toys from the 1950s, many of Japanese origin, now becoming collectable. The bubble car is slightly superior.

*£7 — £10 (locomotive)*
*£5 — £8 (Choo-Choo)*
*£8 — £12 (bubble car)*
*£10 — £15 (veteran car)*

# Sea

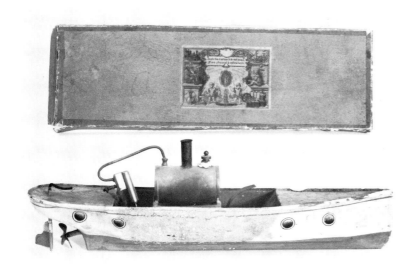

409 From Carette's range of tinplate boats, this scarce steam-driven riverboat is one of their earliest, having a simple oscillating cylinder driving direct to the prop shaft. Finished in cream with scarlet details and lithographed portholes. Shown here with original box. Circa 1900. 34 cm long.

*£800 — £1,200*

410 A late Edwardian four-funnel clockwork torpedo boat by Bing fitted with handrails, two torpedo tubes, bridge, etc. Finished in black and grey. 56 cm long.

*£350 — £500*

411 Difficult to find, this clockwork paddle steamer 'Glasgow' has a mermaid figurehead, and is finished in original red and cream with gilded details. Wound from stern. Circa 1910. 33 cm long.

*£250 — £350*

412 A clockwork torpedo boat, 'H.M.S. Tartar' by Marklin, having three funnels and finished in chocolate and black livery lined in red. Circa 1910. 30.5 cm long.

*£500 — £700*

413 A hot-air spirit-fired torpedo boat, 'H.M.S. Scorpion' by Marklin. Also known as 'Tock Tock' boats, these models had coiled tubing which, when heated by a spirit burner, caused air to be expelled at the rear, producing forward motion. Detachable perforated superstructure with swivelling torpedo tube visible. Finished as previous model. Circa 1910. 41.3 cm long.

*£600 — £800*

414 By an unknown maker, this small clockwork liner of simple construction and appearance displays evidence of age. Circa 1920. 30.5 cm long.

*£35 — £50*

415 The same as the previous model, but in very much better condition.

*£50 — £80*

416 A clockwork 'Dreadnought' battleship of German manufacture having a clockwork mechanism driving eccentric wheels and producing wave motion. Circa 1920. 20 cm long.

*£150 — £180*

417 This small clockwork three-funnel liner has crude superstructure detail and is finished in blue and red. Circa 1920. 23.5 cm.

*£50 — £80*

418 Mounted on wheels, this clockwork battleship No. 244190 is of German manufacture and corkscrews realistically. Circa 1920. 21 cm long.

*£150 — £180*

419 A small clockwork three-funnelled liner finished in blue and red; the masts are missing. Circa 1920. 25.4 cm long.

*£60 — £90*

420 A small Bing two-funnelled clockwork liner with lithographed details, finished in crimson and cream. Circa 1920. 18 cm long.

*£100 — £150*

421 A selection of tinplate nautical items from the early 1920s. Left to right: A clockwork four-funnelled liner with smoke cloud key, finished in red, cream and black. 29.3 cm long. A three-funnelled liner (one funnel and mast missing), having twin screws, finished in red and cream. 25.7 cm long. A twin-funnelled clockwork ship flying red ensign from stern, finished in red, black and cream. 22.8 cm long. A tinplate twin-funnel fly wheel driven model ship, finished in original blue and red paintwork. 25.5. cm long. A clockwork tinplate submarine with handrails, conning tower, etc., finished in original black and battleship grey and lined in gilt. 28.5 cm long.

*£150 — £200 (four-funnelled liner)*
*£80 — £120 (three-funnelled liner)*
*£60 — £90 (twin-funnelled ship)*
*£50 — £75 (model ship)*
*£30 — £40 (submarine)*

422 An Orobr tinplate clockwork liner with battery operated port and starboard lights, one funnel missing. Finished in red and blue with white details and simulated waves. Circa 1925. 32 cm long.

*£75 — £100*

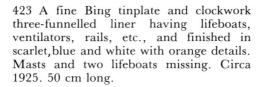

423 A fine Bing tinplate and clockwork three-funnelled liner having lifeboats, ventilators, rails, etc., and finished in scarlet, blue and white with orange details. Masts and two lifeboats missing. Circa 1925. 50 cm long.

*£350 — £500*

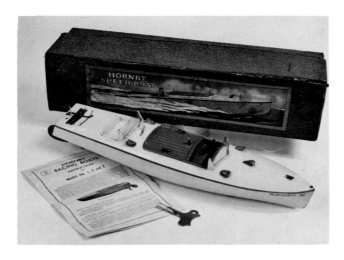

424 A Hornby No. 1 'Hawk' speed boat with clockwork mechanism, here shown with box. 1930s. 24 cm long. Also shown a Hornby 'Racer III' speed boat with box and instructions. 42 cm long.

*£20 — £30 ('Hawk')*
*£75 — £125 ('Racer III')*

425 Illustrated in their late pre-war catalogue, this Bassett-Lowke model oil tanker with electric motor (also available with clockwork motor), is well detailed with handrails, lifeboats, masts, ventilators, etc. Price in late 1930s, 9 gns. 74 cm long.

*£150 — £250*

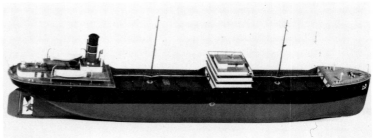

426 A fine scale model of a tug by Bassett-Lowke fitted with electric motor and accurately detailed. Circa late-1930s. 63.5 cm long.

*£200 — £300*

427 Another Bassett-Lowke model, this well detailed clockwork steam launch has wooden hull and super-structure, brass keel strip and nickel plated fittings. Finished in grey with varnished woodwork. Circa 1930. 62.8 cm long mounted on fitted stand.

*£200 — £250*

428 Made by Fleischmann, this good tinplate clockwork liner has an attractively detailed superstructure. Finished in cream with blue and brown trim, it lacks lifeboats, pennant, etc. Circa 1935. 50 cm long.

*£180 — £250*

429 Also by Fleischmann, a similar model this time finished in two-tone brown with cream and scarlet trim. Note lifeboats, additional pennant, etc.

*£200 — £250*

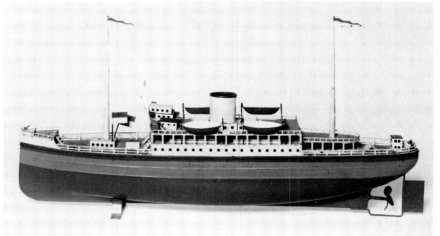

# Air

430 Possibly inspired by a Bleriot, this clockwork mono-plane by Günthermann is mounted on a counter-weighted arm which pivots on a pylon. Flight is induced by a clockwork powered propeller. Circa 1910.

*£300 — £400*

431 Two views of an early toy Zeppelin by Lehmann having a clockwork mechanism powering a large Perspex propeller. The model was intended to be suspended from a length of string, as shown. Also shown with original box. Circa 1915. 18 cm long.

*£150 — £250*

432 Representing an early airliner, this open cockpit single-engined biplane by Günthermann has detachable wings for convenience of packing. Clockwork. Circa 1930. 47 cm long.

*£60 — £90*

433 Related to the constructor car, this Meccano constructor aeroplane came in various forms from No. 00 to No. 2 Special, with a price range between 3s.3d. and 22s.6d. The model illustrated is a No. 1, although most parts were interchangeable. Clockwork motors were available as extras. Circa 1930-40.

*£40 — £60*

434 A 'playworn' example of a Meccano No. 2 constructor aeroplane finished in blue and cream, with British national markings. These models were available in kit form and enabled a child to produce various types of aircraft using a selection of interchangeable parts. A clockwork motor was available as an extra.

*£30 — £50*

435 Produced by Marklin, this model clearly represents the JU52 airliner. The engine nacelles and wheels are missing, and the centre propeller damaged. This was a tri-motor airliner. Sold as a kit, though not as versatile as Meccano's constructor, the model produced was more realistic. Circa 1935. 56 cm wide.

*£100 — £150*

436 A pre-war Japanese TN (Nomura Toys) tri-motor monoplane bomber with a clockwork mechanism which caused the aircraft to travel forwards and activated a sparking machine gun. Propellers missing, paintwork distressed. Circa 1930s.

*£25 — £40*

437 By Burnett, this Ubilda biplane airliner had provisions for electric landing lights (battery carried beneath upper wing), clockwork motor, part nut and bolt construction, and was available in semi-kit form. Circa 1935-40.

*£25 — £40*

438 A late 1930s Frog Interceptor fighter shown here with its box. These 'knock down' models were produced by International Model Aircraft Ltd. and sold by Lines Bros. Available in various national colours and markings, the model shown is finished in camouflage. The box contains a patent high speed winder and is a genuine flying model.

*£20 — £30*

439 Clearly adapted from a piston engined DC3, this 'mint' Mettoy jet airliner has sparking engines and is finished in cream with red and blue markings. Original box. Circa 1955. Wingspan 51 cm.

*£80 — £120*

# Die-cast Transport

The great rival to the tinplate vehicle came in the form of the non-mechanised die-cast toy, normally of a smaller size and popularised by Tootsie Toys in the mid-twenties. These were very popular in America and widely exported, only to be rivalled in the 1930s by the Dinky series, and Britains mainly military die-cast products. The models reasonably faithfully resemble their originals although some artistic licence was exercised, particularly by the U.S. company Manoil.

Various points are worth bearing in mind in this area. Although their first high lead product survives, Dinky's later pre-war models were prone to metal fatigue. Careful examination is required as more highly detailed models may have lost small fittings such as headlights, steering wheels, bumper ends, etc., although many are now available as replacement parts. Pre-war Dinky models generally have smooth wheel hubs although some ridged examples do exist. Do not be influenced by the sight of white tyres (also a pre-war indicator) since they may be replacements, either from post-war French models or modern commercial replacements. Items have often been repainted, either by their original owners, or more recently by enthusiasts with varying degrees of skill. A repainted model can be reduced in value by as much as a third or more. Original catalogues are a great asset in determining originality.

Following Lesney's introduction of Matchbox and Yesteryear models, plastic has played an ever increasing part in construction and has reduced the desirability of these toys to many collectors.

*Value Point*
Original box + + + +

# HORNBY MODELLED MINIATURES
## ADD REALISM TO YOUR RAILWAY

Boys, think how your railways would be improved by the addition of the interesting items shown on this page ! You must have railwaymen to deal with your trains, and passengers to travel in them ; car attendants to look after the passengers, and engineers for the maintenance of the railway and its equipment. You want farmyard animals for lineside fields, and motor vehicles for road traffic. Then you should have at least one of the famous "Hall's Distemper" advertisements alongside your line ! For running on the table when you cannot put down your layout, the miniature train set is exactly what you want. The Modelled Miniatures may be purchased in complete sets as shown or, with the exception of Hall's Distemper Advertisement, they may be purchased separately.

**Guard, Porters, Engineers, Station Master, Hotel Staff, etc.**

**Hikers, Animals, Newsboy, Passengers, Motor Vehicles, etc.**

PRODUCT of MECCANO LIMITED LIVERPOOL

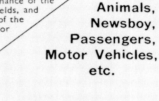

### Modelled Miniatures No. 1 — Station Staff
These splendid models, which are beautifully enamelled in colours, add the final touch of realism to Hornby Station Platforms. The complete set is composed of a Station Master to supervise operations, a Ticket Collector for the station barrier, a Guard giving the "right away" with his whistle and flag, a Locomotive Driver with his oil can, and two Porters, one with luggage and one without. Price, per set, 1/6

### Modelled Miniatures No. 5 — Train and Hotel Staff
Five figures are included in this set, including Pullman Car Conductor, two Pullman Car Waiters and two Hotel Porters. The Car Attendants are conspicuous in smart white jackets, and can be used on trains and in stations. The Hotel Porters, in livery, are essentially for use at important stations. Price, per set, 1/3

### Modelled Miniatures No. 2 — Farmyard Animals
These miniature farmyard animals are useful for placing in lineside fields. The set comprises six animals : Sheep, Pig, two Cows, and two Horses. Price, per set, 1/6

### Modelled Miniatures No. 22 — Motor Vehicles
This very attractive set of model miniatures consists of two Motor Cars, two commercial Vehicles, one Tractor and one Army Tank. The realistic design of each model is clearly shown in the above illustration. Price, per set, 4/-

### Modelled Miniatures No. 13 — Hall's Distemper Advertisement
This miniature of a well-known line-side advertisement is intended to be placed in the fields adjoining the railway track. The two figures are die-cast while the plank they are carrying is of best quality pulp board, attractively printed in two colours. Price 9d.

| SEPARATE PRICES OF MODELLED MINIATURES | | |
|---|---|---|
| Modelled Miniatures Nos. 1, 3, 4 & 5 Figures | each | 3d. |
| Modelled Miniatures No. 2 | | |
| Cow | pair | 7d. |
| Horse | " | 7d. |
| Pig | each | 2d. |
| Sheep | " | 2d. |
| Modelled Miniatures No. 21 | | |
| Loco | each | 9d. |
| Wagon | " | 4d. |
| Crane Truck | " | 6d. |
| Petrol Tank Wagon | " | 6d. |
| Lumber Wagon | " | 5d. |
| Modelled Miniatures No. 22 | | |
| Motor Cars | each | 6d. |
| Commercial Vehicles | " | 8d. |
| Tractor | " | 9d. |
| Tank | " | 1/- |

### Modelled Miniatures No. 3 — Passengers
The various types of passengers to be seen at any railway station are well represented in Modelled Miniatures No. 3. The set contains six figures as illustrated above, comprising Business Man, Male Hiker, Female Hiker, Newsboy, Lady and Mother with Child. They should appear on the station platforms, and they may also be used on lineside roads and fields. Price, per set, 1/6

*Ask your Dealer to show you these Modelled Miniatures*

### Modelled Miniatures No. 4 — Engineering Staff
This set is composed of six figures representing Electrician, two Fitters, Storekeeper, Greaser and Engine Room Attendant. They may be used along the line and on railway premises generally, especially stations, engine sheds and yards. They may also be employed to attend to the miniature motor vehicles. Price, per set, 1/6

**British and Fully Guaranteed**

### Modelled Miniatures No. 21 — Train Set
This Miniature Train Set is a very realistic and attractive model. It is die-cast in hard metal and includes Locomotive, Wagon, Crane Truck, Lumber Wagon and "Shell" Petrol Tank Wagon, complete in detail and perfect in finish. Price 2/6

**Beautifully Finished in bright colours**

Manufactured by Meccano Ltd., Binns Road, Liverpool 13

440 One of the earliest British made die-cast vehicles, is this Britains steam roller. Motion could be obtained by attaching cord to flywheel. Finished in green with black, red and gold. Unnamed. Circa 1908. 8 cm long.

*£60 — £100*

441 The American firm Tootsie Toys introduced a range of die-cast vehicles in 1925. Shown here is a delivery van with perforated lattice sides.

*£30 — £50*

442 A Graham Paige town sedan by Tootsie Toys. Note the similarity of this and the previous model to the later Dinky equivalents, 22 and 28 series vans, and the 24 series town sedan. 1930s.

*£20 — £30 (Tootsie)*
*£100 — £200 (Dinky)*

Left: This December 1933 advertisement from *The Meccano Magazine* introduced Dinky Toy motor vehicles, at that time called Modelled Miniatures. Available as a set were those illustrated centre left; also shown in Colour Plate 32, page 124.

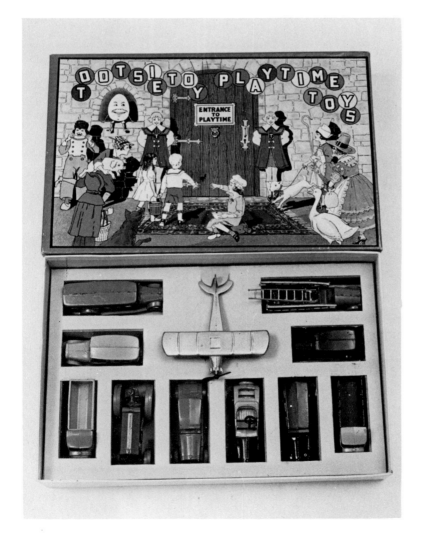

443 From one of their boxed sets, these eleven Tootsie Toy models give an indication of the wide range available on the other side of the Atlantic in the early 1930s. The set comprises a Buick saloon, a Buick coupé and Buick tourer; a Ford saloon, two Mack-type trucks, a yellow taxi, tractor, a coach, a fire-engine with three detachable ladders, together with a high-wing monoplane.

*£500 — £600 (set as shown)*
*£35 — £50 (individual models)*

444 The American firm of Manoil produced a small range of futuristic models in the 1930s — shown here is a coupé. It is interesting to note that wooden wheels were used on these models.

*£15 — £20*

445 Another futuristic Manoil car, rubber tyres missing.

*£20 — £30*

446 Lacking its hook, this breakdown truck has side mounted spare wheels, a popular feature of the 1930s. The headlamps are cast into the body not the wings, as in the previous two Manoil items.

*£15 — £20*

447 Three mint examples from a boxed set by John Hill & Co. comprising a French Char tank with rubber track, a mobile anti-aircraft gun and a mobile searchlight. Note similarity to Tootsie casting. 1930s.

*£30 — £50 (the set)*

448 By John Hill & Co., this Irving Napier Golden Arrow record car was made c.1929, and was available with rubber or metal wheels.

*£75 — £100*

449 Probably also by John Hill & Co., this model of Malcolm Campbell's famous 'Bluebird' record car is of heavy construction. Note the similarity of windscreen treatment to previous model.

*£75 — £100*

450 Possibly by Plank, this World War I staff car has attractive fittings, starting handle, steering wheel, mounted horn and headlights. Note the anti-decapitation bar.

*£40 — £60*

*Colour Plate 34. A good set of 38 series Dinky sports cars. (See also 502, page 165.)*

*Colour Plate 35. A selection of Dinky 30 and 36 series cars including Rolls Royce, Daimler, two Vauxhalls, Rover, Bentley, Humber and Armstrong Siddeley, 1940s.*

*£15 — £20 (each)*

451 From left to right, and World War I in concept, a Britains D series armoured car, a Taylor and Barrett ambulance, and a Tootsie Toy Char tank. Circa 1925.

*£10 — £15 (armoured car)*
*£15 — £20 (ambulance and tank)*

452 A selection of small model cars mainly from the 1930s. In the foreground, although lacking windscreen, radiator, driver and passenger, this Britains sports car is still a desirable item. Left to right: a Tootsie toy streamlined saloon, Manoil breakdown truck, Tootsie 'Graham Paige', Minic racing car and two Timpo racing cars.

*£25 — £40 (sports car)*
*£15 — £25 (Tootsie saloon)*
*£15 — £20 (breakdown truck, 'Graham Paige', Minic racing car)*
*£2 — 3 (Timpo racing cars)*

453 By Gaiety toys this three-wheeled Aero Morgan sports car captures the sporting feeling. Solid rubber front wheels, clockwork powered.

*£30 — £50*

454 A scarce and interesting German made clockwork coupé, having an ingenious mechanism which activates the steering in six different ways. Here shown with its original box. Circa 1935.

*£25 — £40*

456 A scarce but playworn example of Britains coupé. The presence of a spare wheel on this example is misleading and is certainly a later (unofficial) addition, probably from a Tootsie Toy. The open sports car shows considerable evidence of wear, lacking its radiator and windscreen. Early examples of these models had smooth tyres; later editions white with tread, black post-war. (See also page 153 for original catalogue illustration.)

*£40 — £60 (coupé as shown)*     *£25 — £40 (sports car as shown)*

*Colour Plate 36. From a boxed set, ten fine late 19th century die-cast cavalry models probably by Heyde, Germany, with detachable heads and saddles. Approx. 10 cm high.*

*£150 — £200*

*Colour Plate 37. A selection of Britains model soldiers. Left to right: Highland piper, Togoland warrior, Zulu with knob-kerrie, lying Vickers machine gunner, British infantry arms slope, Australian infantry arms slope, French infantry arms slope, German infantry arms slope, Scots Guard arms slope.*

*£1.50 — £3 (each)*

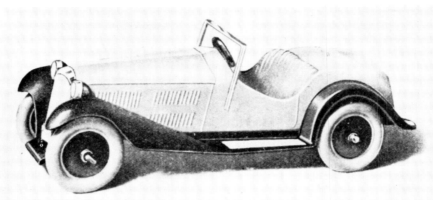

No. 1398   Sports Model Open Tourer.   Finished Various Colours,
Rubber tyred.   Measures 4¼ ins. long by 1¾ ins. wide **1s. 0d. each.**

No. 1399   Two-Seater Coupé Model, fitted Bumpers.   Finished Various Colours.
Rubber tyred.   Measures 4½ ins. long by 1¾ ins. wide.   **1s. 0d. each.**

No. 1413   Mobile Police with Two Officers.   Rubber tyred.   Measures 4¼ ins. long.   As Illustrated.
**1s. 6d. each.**

MANUFACTURED BY   *W Britain*   IN LONDON ENGLAND
TRADE   Regd No 459993   MARK

455   For the benefit of the toy shop proprietors, Britains produced a large well-illustrated catalogue. From their 1938 edition are these die-cast cars, the coupé being particularly difficult to find. Prices are for mint examples.

| | | |
|---|---|---|
| £100 — £150 (tourer) | £200 — £300 (coupé) | £80 — £120 (police car) |
| £200 — £300 (boxed) | £300 — £400 (boxed) | £180 — £250 (boxed) |

457 Produced shortly before the Second World War, Britains introduced this model of John Cobb's Railton record car. As in the real car, the body lifts off to expose interesting chassis, engine detail, etc. The previous model, the Bluebird, had the same detachable body feature.

*£200 — £300*

458 From Britains extensive range of military die-cast toys, left, a miniature balloon barrage unit with the winch lorry (cab roof detached) connected to a lead balloon. To complement this model, Britain produced a gas cylinder lorry and trailer. Centre, a mobile searchlight with draw bar for use with lorries and, right, a Bren gun carrier complete with three-man crew.

*£25 — £40*
*(balloon barrage unit as shown)*
*£60 — £100*
*(mint unit)*
*£18 — £25*
*(searchlight)*
*£12 — £18*
*(bren gun carrier)*

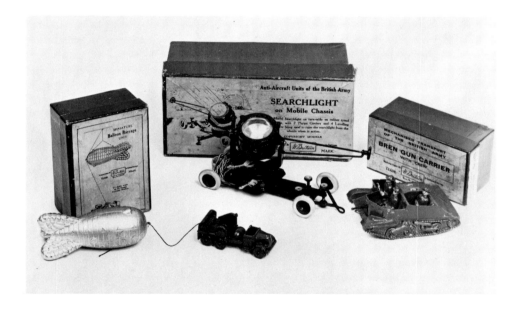

459 A British Army covered tender half-truck lorry by Britains, here shown with box bearing early wartime 'temporary packaging' additional label. Driver missing.

*£40 — £60*

460 This Britains staff car was produced both before and after the last war. The black tyres, if original, indicate that the model is post-war. The pre-war car had white tyres. (Catalogue no. 1448; see catalogue illustration for civilian versions.)

*£75 — £125*
*£100 — £200 (with original box)*

461 Showing evidence of metal fatigue, this Dinky Toys *Queen Mary* displays attractive packaging. By this time, c.1935, Dinky boasted over 150 varieties. Also by Dinky, an *Empress of Britain,* and from the British Navy range H.M.S. *Hood,* H.M.S. *Nelson,* H.M.S. *York* and H.M.S. *Delhi.*

*£5 — £8 (Queen Mary)*
*£3 — £5 (Empress of Britain)*
*£5 — £10 (H.M.S. Hood)*
*£2 — £5 (others)*

462 A selection of 1930 die-cast model aircraft. During this period tin was used for the main wings in association with die-cast bodies. First three on left, a cabin monoplane, an autogiro and a two-seater monoplane, are examples from the French Dinky range. Centre below: a Tootsie Toy U.S. army monoplane. Right below, a high wing monoplane by Tootsie Toy. Centre and right top, two copies of the preceding Tootsie toy, this time by a British manufacturer.

*£8 — £12 (monoplane)    £5 — £8 (U.S. monoplane)*
*£12 — £15 (autogiro)    £5 — £8 (high wing monoplane)*
*£8 — £12 (two-seater)    £3 — £5 (Tootsie Toy copies)*

463 A Dinky pre-war Mayo composite aircraft showing display box and gliding instructions. This model illustrates well the effects of serious metal fatigue. The box states that, by the time of introduction, over 300 varieties were available; pencilled price 2s. (10p).

*£20 — £30 (as shown)*
*£70 — £100 (sound example)*

464 Shown here from Dinky's range of aircraft, an Armstrong Whitworth Whitley bomber with original box; note the metal fatigue promoting additional dihedral to wings; a souvenir model of a Percival Gull used in record breaking flight with original box; and a Junkers JU89 heavy bomber.

*£10 — £15 (Whitley)*
*£25 — £40 (Gull)*
*£15 — £20 (Junkers)*

465 A further selection of Dinky aircraft, shown on a half-dozen Bristol Blenheim box with interesting wartime box lid description. Left to right, top to bottom: a de Havilland Comet Racer; a Hawker Hurricane in silver pre-war finish with under-carriage; a Bristol Blenheim Mark IV bomber; a Gloster Gladiator fighter; an Airspeed Envoy airliner.

*£5 — £8 (Comet)*
*£8 — £12 (Hawker Hurricane)*
*£7 — £10 (Bristol Blenheim)*
*£8 — £12 (Gloster Gladiator)*
*£7 — £10 (Airspeed Envoy)*

466 This Dinky B17 die-cast model has revolving tinplate propeller and is typical of the range c.1940-48.

*£5 — £8*

467 From the no. 22 series, a Dinky 22A sports car, windscreen damaged, finished in scarlet and cream, with solid wheels, tinplate radiator surround. These models are not subject to metal fatigue found in late Dinky models as they have a high lead content. Circa 1934.

*£150 — £200*

468 A 22B from the Dinky no. 22 series, a model SS 1 or 2 coupé. The model is very brightly finished in yellow and bright green paintwork and again a tinplate radiator surround is used.

*£200 — £300*

469 22C, a motor truck (possibly inspired by Bedford) finished in blue with red back, tinplate radiator surround.

*£175 — £250*

470 22D, a delivery van. This model used the same cab and chassis as the previous model but incorporated a van-type back. Finished in blue and orange.

*£175 — £250*

471 22E, a tractor. This model bears a strong resemblance to the then current Fordson Standard. Painted in yellow and blue with red wheels.

*£60 — £100*

472 22F; the tank was probably copied with licence from a Medium tank Mark III. Finished in bright green with revolving orange turret.

*£60 — £100*

473 From the Dinky 24 series this ambulance has been repainted, the headlamps are missing and tyres have been replaced. Note the high cutaway front wings and open side windows; a later version of this in the 30 series has closed side windows and later type chassis with lower front wings and side lamps. A criss-cross chassis is found on 24 series vehicles.

*£40 — £75 (as shown)*

474 This Dinky 24 series super streamlined saloon displays metal fatigue to chassis, headlamps missing (replacement chassis and radiators are now available).

*£20 — £30 (as shown)*

475 A Dinky 25 series first pattern market gardener's lorry. The Carter Paterson tin roof is from another 25 series vehicle. This model should have a tinplate radiator; note cracking to original tyres.

*£20 — £30 (as shown)*

476 A rare first pattern 28 series delivery van in blue with 'Oxo' transfers. These early models were not subject to metal fatigue since they had very high lead content. Note solid wheels and tyres. Circa 1935.

*£160 — £220 (as shown)*

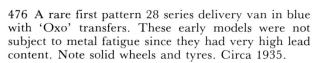

477 Advertising *The Manchester Guardian,* this 28 series first pattern delivery van is in excellent condition considering its age; scarce. Circa 1935.

*£200 — £300*

478 The Dinky 22 series van later became the basis for 28 series vans painted and transferred in various company colours and introduced in 1935. Second pattern one piece casting, original price 6d. (2½ p). The colour photograph clearly shows evidence of metal fatigue, a problem frequently encountered on 28 series second type vans. Finished in red with black edged gold lettering. Pre-war. (See also Colour Plate 33, page 124.)

*£80 — £100*

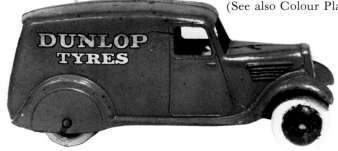

479 A Dinky 28 series second pattern 'Hornby Trains' van. This model retains much original finish; plated wheels.

*£120 — £200 (as shown)*

480 A Dinky 28 series second type Pickfords van, which although over forty years old retains good transfers.

*£120 — £200*

481 A 28 series van, second type, repainted. Without original finish, transfer, etc., value is considerably reduced.

*£25 — £40 (as shown)*

482 Two examples of the same 30 series Dinky Rolls Royce. Left: an early version with smooth wheels and white rubber tyres. Made pre-war, this model displays fatigue damage, and the radiator is missing (often present in pre-war models). Above: an intact post-war model, although the tyres are missing.

*£5 — £8 (pre-war, as shown)*
*£12 — £18 (post-war, as shown)*

483 30 series Chrysler Airflow saloon. The front bumper is missing on the model illustrated; this is a not uncommon fault as these were fragile.

*£40 — £60 (as shown)*

484 Of very similar appearance to the previous example, this 22G tourer lacks a windscreen, and the considerable paint damage is consistent with age.

*£50 — £80 (as shown)*

485 This pre-war model of a 30 series Daimler saloon well illustrates how rubber can deteriorate with age.

*£18 — £25 (as shown)*

486 The post-war version of 30 series Daimler; note the ridged wheels.

*£12 — £18 (as shown)*

487 This 30 series ambulance illustrates points made on 473. Note the Bentley-type radiator; the 24 series of vehicles used one radiator type for all vehicles of non-identified type.

*£10 — £15 (as shown)*

488 This 36 series Rover saloon uses a similar body casting to 474. Note the Rover-type radiator and more fully enveloping mudguards.

*£12 — £18 (as shown)*

489 This pre-war 38 series Alvis tourer lacks steering wheel, windscreen and headlamps.

*£5 — £10 (as shown)*

490 A pre-war double-decker bus; the fatigued wheels retaining their original tyres. These models had short staircases, not present on post-war models.

*£25 — £40 (as shown)*

491 A similar model, repainted with advertisements missing, this pre-war double-decker bus has reduced value to the Dinky collector. Buses have a following who often repaint them in local liveries.

*£15 — £20 (as shown)*

492 A streamlined coach of pre-war manufacture which, although not visible, has smooth wheels, open rear window.

*£12 — £20 (as shown)*

493 The scarce Royal Air Mail service car finished in blue, but with fatigue cracks. This model was only produced pre-war.

*£30 — £40 (as shown)*

494 A Royal Air Mail service car retaining most of its original finish with little trace of fatigue. Unperished tyres are very scarce.

*£100 — £150*

495 This scarce Dinky pressure refueller bears 'Shell Aviation Service' transfers. Solid rubber wheels.

*£50 — £75 (as shown)*

496 A G.W.R. mechanical horse and covered trailer. The trailer chassis has 'grown' slightly with fatigue and the windscreen pillars on the mechanical horse are missing. Circa 1937.

*£30 — £50 (as shown)*

497 Another example of metal fatigue, this time on a Hotchkiss racing car. The front apron is completely disintegrated and the tyres are replacements. Pre-war.

*£10 — £15 (as shown)*

498 A Mercedes pre-war racing car. It has been repainted and has non-original tyres, the original tyres being white with herringbone tread.

*£5 — £10 (as shown)*

499 Although originally numbered 32, the Chrysler Airflow is normally thought of as a 1930s series model, and as such is no. 30A. Available pre- and post-war, the radiator grille and rear bumper are fragile separate castings and frequently found damaged. Finished in various colours. Post-war model shown.

*£75 — £110 (pre-war)*
*£50 — £80 (post-war)*

501 From the 36 series of Dinkys this Salmson two-seater sports car, although a post-war model, has white tyres. It is also available in four-seater form.

*£15 — £20*

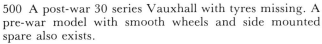

500 A post-war 30 series Vauxhall with tyres missing. A pre-war model with smooth wheels and side mounted spare also exists.

*£30 — £50 (pre-war)*
*£14 — £18 (post-war)*

502 A set of Dinky post-war 38 series sports and touring cars, the Armstrong Siddeley replacing the elusive Triumph Dolomite. The SS 100 suffers damage more easily owing to lips on the front wings. (See also Colour Plate 34, page 149.)

*£15 — £20 (each)*

503 From the 38 series, this Dinky Jaguar SS100 sports car was the only model in the range having aero screens. The leading edges of the front wings are fragile and one is frequently missing. Produced late pre-war and early post-war, the pre-war models have silver base plates.

*£12 — £20*

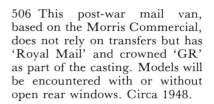

504 In this instance the cut-away near window on a London taxi does not indicate a pre-war model. Note significant ridged wheels. Circa 1947.

*£10 — £15 (as shown)*

505 A post-war London taxi. This model has cast interior detail including a driver. Non-voided rear window, tyres missing.

*£10 — £15*

506 This post-war mail van, based on the Morris Commercial, does not rely on transfers but has 'Royal Mail' and crowned 'GR' as part of the casting. Models will be encountered with or without open rear windows. Circa 1948.

*£8 — £12*

507 Two examples of the Dinky Standard Vanguard saloon originally offered with cut-away rear wheel arch, and slight casting differences to boot.

*£7 — £10 (earlier)*
*£4 — £6 (later)*

508  A selection of 1950 Dinky sports and sports racing cars. Top left to right: an Aston Martin DB3S (racing finish), an Austin Healey 100 sports (racing finish), an MG Midget (racing finish). Bottom left to right: a Sunbeam Alpine sports (racing finish), a TR2 sports (touring finish) with spun aluminium wheels and late pattern box, and an MG Midget sports (touring finish, i.e. the driver does not wear racing overalls or crash helmet as in the racing model).

*£12 — £18 (each boxed)*
*£7 — £10 (each unboxed)*

509  A selection of Dinky toy vehicles available in the late 1940s and early 1950s. All but 'Chivers Jellies' Trojan van and observation coach had pre-war counterparts.

*£3 — £30*

510 Trojan vans are also collected for their advertising. This model has smooth front wheels and ridged rear wheels, this having no bearing upon age, but is due to a casting error or old smooth wheels being used up.

*£15 — £20*

511 A good example of a Dinky Trojan 'Esso' van. Other liveries were Dunlop, Chivers, Cydrax, Brooke Bond; an Oxo livery was issued from 1953-54 only and is therefore scarcer than the others.

*£30 — £40 (Oxo)*
*£20 — £30 (other transfers)*

512 Enhanced by its original box, this Studebaker land cruiser retains excellent original finish. Early 1950s.

*£6 — £10*

513 By the late 1950s moulded Perspex windscreens had appeared. This Packard convertible typifies the sizeable proportions of American cars.

*£7 — £10*

514 Shortly after the war a range of Supertoys was introduced. Illustrated here is a Foden 14-ton tanker displaying early pattern radiator, wheels, tyres, etc., and complete with its original box.

*£30 — £50 (original box)*
*£20 — £30 (without box)*

515 A scarce Guy 'Slumberland' van with original box. Advertising normally enhances the value of an item. Early 1950s. This van also carries 'Ever-Ready', 'Weetabix', and 'Golden Shred' advertisements.

*£70 — £110*

516 From the Supertoy range introduced post-war, a selection of lorries. Left to right: Leyland Comet, Foden flat truck, Bedford articulated lorry. Early 1950s.

*£10 — £15 (Leyland Comet)*
*£20 — £30 (Foden)*
*£10 — £15 (Bedford)*

517 Left to right: Foden 14-ton tanker with first pattern radiator, 'Dinky Service' breakdown lorry, Dinky Foden diesel 8-wheel wagon with early pattern herringbone tyres, no tow-hook, early type box.

*£30 — £50 (tanker)*
*£8 — £12 (breakdown lorry)*
*£25 — £35 (wagon and early type box)*

**518** The Coventry Climax fork lift truck was another popular model. The handle elevates the fork. Late pattern box, this model was originally no. 14c. Sold for 8s.1d. (40½ p) in 1952.

*£5 — £8*

**519** The Blaw Knox bulldozer was a popular long term production item. Note the original price on box indicating an early 1950s' model; it was later renumbered and sold for 13s. (65p) in 1956.

*£7 — £10*

**520** Using the same casting as the Blaw Knox bulldozer this heavy tractor has rubber creeper tracks.

*£7 — £10*

**521** A brainchild of toy marketing came in the form of Lesney's reasonably priced diminutive die-cast models in 'Matchbox' containers. Introduced in the 1950s, these models from the original series are now highly collectable, some being already much scarcer than others due to popularity of form or fragility of construction. Shown here are Nos. 1-8 with their original boxes.

| No. 1 | Aveling Barford road roller | £6 — £10 | No. 6 | Euclid quarry dumper | £6 — £10 |
| No. 2 | Muir Hill dumper | £6 — £10 | No. 7 | Horse drawn milk cart | £10 — £15 |
| No. 3 | Cement mixer | £5 — £8 | No. 8 | D8 caterpillar tractor | £6 — £10 |
| No. 4 | Massey-Harris tractor | £6 — £10 | | | |
| No. 5 | Double-decker bus | £6 — £10 | | Prices are all based on boxed models. | |

522 Again with marketing inspired presentation, Lesney produced the Matchbox Constructors Gift Set, comprising seven vehicles. Note however that these are later types with plastic wheels and are of larger size than the early models.

*£20 — £30 (for set)*

523 Some of the most popular post-war models were Lesney's 'Yesteryear' series. Illustrated are a London tram and a 'B' type bus, both bearing advertisements. Circa 1960.

*£12 — £18 (each, boxed)*
*£8 — £12 (each, unboxed)*

524 Although of post-war manufacture, the Lesney Massey-Harris 745D tractor is difficult to find. Shown here with original box with price 17s.6d. (87½ p). 20 cm long.

*£150 — £200*

525 More a model than a toy, this Chad Valley Fordson Major Tractor was retailed by agricultural retailers, Ford agents, etc. It was available with Firestone or Goodyear tyres and had a realistic starting handle which wound the clockwork mechanism. Finished in dark blue and orange. Circa 1950.

*£100 — £150*

526 One of the scarcer post-war models, this Tri-ang 'Spot-on' Austin prime mover with articulated flat float and M.G.A. in crate is shown with its original box. Circa late 1950s.

*£20 — £30*

527 Inspired by Enid Blyton, these models were produced by Bridgie and Morestone. Amusing models, the vehicles are die-cast and the figures plastic. Left to right: boxed engine with Noddy, boxed train with Noddy and Big Ears, boxed Big Ears on bicycle, boxed Noddy and his car.

*£3 — £5 (Noddy in train)*
*£5 — £8 (Noddy and Big Ears)*
*£5 — £8 (Big Ears on bicycle)*
*£10 — £15 (Noddy in car)*

# Die-cast Miscellaneous

The early period of production of these items, 1870-1900, was dominated by German manufacturers who produced flat and semi-flat soldiers. The role of leading producer and innovator was then assumed by Britains who pioneered the hollow cast technique and introduced a wide range of military figures. These were followed by accessories for the model railway enthusiast, together with farm and zoo items, gardens, cowboys and Indians.

Britains early production models had oval bases with applied paper labels, now rare. Later models have rectangular bases with cast raised copyright dates. Dating of models is not easy and an appreciation of modifications in military uniforms, for example putties and tin helmets, is useful. Britains products are nearly always found bearing their name and because of their popularity are valued more highly than models from other companies such as Hill & Co., Taylor & Barratt, Skybirds, etc. Various gauges are encountered and an illustration from Britains catalogue is included (overleaf) to show this.

Soldiers are the most sought after models but garden and farm items are gaining in popularity, with zoo and cowboy models the least popular.

In the 1960s Britains and other manufacturers ceased production of lead soldiers in favour of plastic, though model soldiers as opposed to toys are still made in lead.

With such frail items, particularly when used for their intended purpose (i.e. to be shot at with projectiles), damage is not infrequent. Broken heads and limbs therefore, which require great skill to repair successfully, greatly diminish value. Also, examine carefully for traces of oxidisation, initially evident by dulling of paint.

*Value Point*
Original box + + + +

# MODELS MANUFACTURED
# BY BRITAINS LIMITED

conform to the following scales.

The measurement given is that of an ordinary Infantryman (without headgear). All other models, Cavalry, etc., are proportionate.

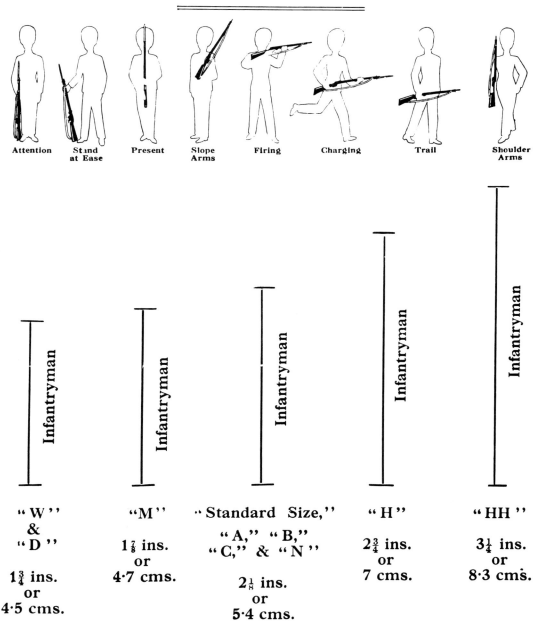

|  |  |  |  |  |  |  |  |
|---|---|---|---|---|---|---|---|
| **Attention** | **Stand at Ease** | **Present** | **Slope Arms** | **Firing** | **Charging** | **Trail** | **Shoulder Arms** |

**Infantryman** "W" & "D" 1¾ ins. or 4·5 cms.

**Infantryman** "M" 1⅞ ins. or 4·7 cms.

**Infantryman** "Standard Size," "A," "B," "C," & "N" 2⅛ ins. or 5·4 cms.

**Infantryman** "H" 2¾ ins. or 7 cms.

**Infantryman** "HH" 3¼ ins. or 8·3 cms.

This scale guide, reprinted from Britains pre-war catalogue, illustrates scales and positions of their range and is particularly useful for identifying other than standard sizes.

528 These 'flats' of Prussian Infantry and mounted officer in the style of the 1750s were produced by the Nuremberg firm of Ernst Heinrichsen, c.1890. Highly suitable for war games and authentic recreation of famous battles. All manner of accessories, including trees, palisades, gun carriages, etc., were available. Note the oval wood box with its original labels.

*£40 — £60 (set of 25 with box)*

529 Not only model soldiers were produced by Heinrichsen; here is a delightful 'flat' locomotive with carriages together with a selection of various figures including workman with wheelbarrow, lady with parasol, etc. Late 19th century.

*£30 — £40 (train set)*
*£1 (each)*

530 Great character is displayed in these German flats depicting soldiers and peasants in 16th century costume. Note the perched cockerel, and the rabbit hanging from the soldier's halberd. Late 19th century.

*£1.50 — £3 (each)*

531 Another group of German flats with soldiers and village figures. The reality of the scene is completed with the figure hanging from the gibbet and soldiers merrymaking with wenches.

*£1.50 — £3 (each)*

532 Ten Garde du Corps at the charge, Heinrichsen. Circa 1890. Original box not shown.

*£40 — £60 (set of 10)*

533 From a boxed set, probably by Heyde, Germany, and comprising forty-five pieces. Cavalry, band, marching arms slope, gun team. Late 19th century.

*£100 — £150 (set)*

*Colour Plate 38. Made popular by the 1930s' Disney films, Britains produced this colourful die-cast Snow White and the Seven Dwarfs. Circa 1938.*

*£60 — £80 (set)*
*£25 — £35 (repainted)*

*Colour Plate 39. A Britains Fordson Major tractor, mounted on spudded metal wheels, cat. no. 127F. Circa 1948. 10 cm long. These models were produced with fine detail and are difficult to find in good and complete condition.*

*£80 — £100 (with box)*

*Colour Plate 40. Another variation of Britains Fordson tractor is this model with later type balloon-tyred front wheels, and later thinner parallel steering column, cat. no. 128F. Circa 1948.*

*£60 — £80*

534 Four sets of boxed Britains cavalry from immediate post-war period. Top to bottom: Royal Scots Greys, box no. 32; Indian Lancers, box no. 66; French Cuirassiers, box no. 138; Imperial Russian Cossacks, box no. 136.

*£35 — £60 (per box)*

535 Four further sets of boxed Britains, again immediate post-war period. Top to bottom: American Civil War Confederate cavalry, box no. 2055; Egyptian cavalry, box no. 115; 12th Royal Lancers, box no. 2076; 7th Queen's Own Hussars, box no. 2075.

*£35 — £60 (per box)*

536 Britains soldiers from the Boer War period. Shown here the plain oval base type with stuck on paper copyright label. Labels were used for a very short period, being superseded by cast copyright dates, and later rectangular bases with cast copyright dates became the standard form.

*£12 — £18 (oval base with label)*
*£4 — £7 (oval base without label)*

537 'Firing lying down': The Gordon Highlanders, Britains cat. no. 118. Nine soldiers with rifles, and a kneeling spotter with articulated arms, holding binoculars; normally only eight pieces were included in this box. Note the original box listing the regiment's battle honours. Circa 1910, but had a long catalogue appearance.

*£30 — £50 (with original box)*
*£16 — £24 (without box)*

538 A Britains military band comprising eight pieces and officer. Circa 1920.

*£30 — £40 (set)*

539 A Britains standard bearer together with six line infantry with slope arms.

*£3 — £5 (standard bearer)*
*£15 — £22 (set of 6 infantry)*

540 A selection of Britains pre-war soldiers including, left to right: scarce Royal Company of Archers, standing with bow, and firing bow; sailors marching; French Foreign Legionnaires, rifles with fixed bayonets; Continental (possibly Italian) marching soldier with rifle at slope.

*£4 (each Archer)*
*£2 (each sailor)*
*£2 (each Legionnaire)*
*£3 (marching soldier)*

541 Together with their boxes: top Britains no. 1554 Royal Canadian Mounted Police, dismounted, in regulation summer dress, with officer (eight figures). Below a set of seven Australian infantry (marching arms slope) with rifles, plus officer.

*£30 — £40 (set R.C.M.P.)*
*£30 — £40 (set infantry)*

542 Two larger Britains box sets. Top, Life Guards and 4th Hussars, box no. 50; below, Danish Army (full dress), box no. 2018.

*£45 — £75 (per box)*

543 An interesting boxed set by Johillco containing a variety of mounted soldiers, machine gunners and standard bearers. It is the presence of the scarce box that makes this item collectable; otherwise the soldiers do not have the Britains appeal.

*£18 — £25 (boxed set)*

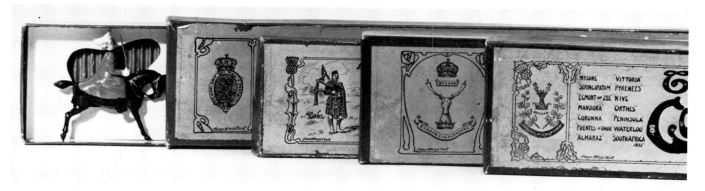

544 Note the name 'Fred Whisstock' as designer of the labels on these pre-war Britain boxes. The presence of an original box enhances considerably the price of a set.

545 Together with its post-war box, a Britains R.H.A. six-horse gun team with late type gun. Note team walking; for galloping team see 553. The team 'at halt' is scarce.

*£100 — £125 (mint boxed)*

546 A complete Royal Field Artillery gun team of six walking horses with three postillions, limber with two seated figures and field gun, Britains. Circa 1914. Note horses' ears cast as one, and harness variation indicating early models; the cannon is of simple construction without sophistication of protective shield.

*£120 — £160*

547 Britains Royal Army Corps ambulance wagon showing the canvas canopy in semi-collapsed state, nurses and a group of stretcher bearers. Circa 1914. By 1938 nurses' skirts had risen exposing the ankles.

*£60 — £80 (wagon)*
*£15 — £20 (nurses, bearers)*

548 A Britains open Army Service Corps wagon, no. 146, with postillion and four seated soldiers. Normally this model came with only two seated soldiers. Circa 1914.

*£40 — £60*

182

549 This galloping six-horse team gun carriage has three postillions, each with whip, and a limber, c.1920. The field gun is later and this style of Britains field gun was largely unchanged until 1955. This example has damage to horses' legs.

*£80 — £120*

550 Another six-horse gun team with original cannon, here showing a kneeling soldier with shell and a kneeling officer. Circa 1920. A better example than the above item

*£100 — £140 (gun team)*
*£2 (each kneeling figure)*

551 Foreground a Royal Horse Artillery walking gun team, and behind a Royal Field Artillery gun team. Both Britains. 1920s.

*£90 — £130 (R.H.A.)*
*£80 — £120 (R.F.A.)*

552 A converted Britains model representing a German gun team.

*£50 — £80*

553 A galloping gun team of the Royal Horse Artillery flanked by escort, three with carbines and officer with sabre. Britains. Circa 1930.

*£100 — £150*

554 Shown with their original box, a set of four lancers and officer with sabre of the 21st Empress of India's Lancers. Britains no. 100.

*£100 — £150 (set as shown with box)*

555 A further selection of Britains mounted soldiers, left to right: pre-World War I officer, 1st Life Guards; Dragoon Guard with lance; Egyptian Camel Corps; Lancer with foreign service helmet, pre-World War I; Egyptian lancer; Skinner's Horse Sowar; Hussar officer with sabre.

£6 — £8 (Life Guard)          £4 — £7 (Egyptian Lancer)
£4 — £7 (Dragoon Guard)       £4 — £7 (Sowar)
£4 — £7 (Camel Corps)         £4 — £7 (Hussar)
£10 — £15 (Lancer with helmet)

556 An officer and four troopers of the First Dragoons wearing tropical uniforms. The officer is wearing boots, the O.R.s. puttees. Britains.

£25 — £40

557 A selection of Britains cavalry showing Cossacks and Spanish Lancers.

£4 — £6 (each)

558 Four Britains 9th Lancers together with mounted officer.

*£30 — £40*

559 Britains 3rd Dragoon Guards comprising officer with sabre and four troopers with carbines. The officers' horses often appear in contrasting colours to their troopers.

*£30 — £40*

560 Four mounted Britains Indian Lancers together with bugler and three 2nd Dragoon Guards with lances.

*£4 — £6 (each)*

561 Left to right: two galloping Hussars, and a Lancers officer with two Lancers. Britains.
*£4 — £6 (each Hussar)*     *£10 — £15 (officer)*     *£4 — £7 (each Lancer)*

562 Twelve piece band of the Life Guards. Britains.

*£80 — £120*

563 A selection of Britains North American Indians and cowboys. Some figures have articulated arms.

*£1 — £2 (each, on foot)*
*£2 — £3 (each, mounted)*

564 Britains pre-war railway accessories: the lady railway traveller flanked by a guard with articulated right arm holding lamp, a porter (trolley not shown) and a selection of trunks, golf club bags, etc. Britains 5.4 cm models were ideally suited to gauge I railway layouts.

*£2 (lady traveller)*
*£1.50 — £2 (each guard and porter)*

565 From the Britains range of military toys comes this 'anti-aircraft predictor' complete with operator. Cat. no. 1728. Introduced shortly before World War II.

*£12 — £15 (with box)*

566 Looking rather uncomfortable, this Britains observer, with articulated arm holding binoculars, lies back in his rotating spotting chair. Cat. no. 1731. Circa 1939.

*£4 — £7*
*£8 — £12 (with box)*

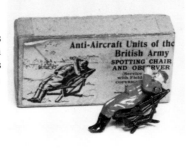

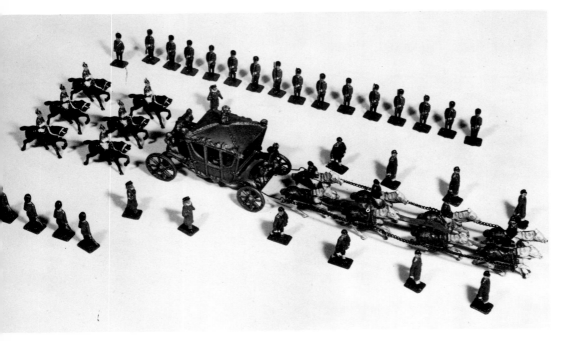

567 One of Britains great rivals in model soldier manufacture were John Hill & Co., whose founder had once worked for Britains. Here is one of Hill's more prestigious productions, a 1937 Coronation coach drawn by eight horses with postillions, complete with footmen, Yeomen of the Guard, Life Guards.

*£75 — £100*

568 A Britains 1953 Coronation coach, together with eight horses and postillions and original fitted box. Contrary to popular belief this model was produced long after the Coronation, through the 1950s into the 1960s.

*£75 — £100 (boxed set)*

569 To go with their range of military vehicles, Skybirds and Dinky produced these figures of airmen. Circa 1940.

*£1 (each)*

570 A further extension of Britains range were these circus performers complete with ringmaster. Also shown is a Britains model farm set, with boxes.

*£60 — £80 (mammoth circus)*
*£15 — £25 (model farm)*

571 After the horror of World War I, Britains, Hill and Co. and others produced, in addition to military pieces (which for a period fell from favour), farm, zoo and garden models. From Britains range of Home Farm Series comes this 'Tree and Gate with swing and boy'. No. 19F, it is still fairly common, but always desirable with its original box. Circa 1938.

*£8 — £12*
*£15 — £20 (with original box)*

572 Britains farm wagon (tailgate missing), cat. no. 5F, and complete with two horses and drover, is from their Home Farm Series. Also shown, cat. no. 9F, a horse roller complete with horse and leader.

£40 — £50 (5F)
£25 — £40 (9F)

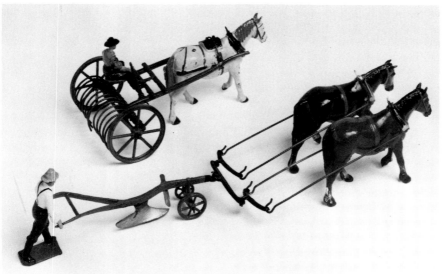

573 Catalogue no. 8F relates to Britains horse drawn hayrake, here shown complete with driver. Below is the general purpose horse drawn plough, cat. no. 6F complete with two horses and ploughman.

£25 — £40 (8F)
£25 — £40 (6F)

574 Again from Britains Home Farm Series, this tumbrel cart, cat. no. 4F, complete with horse and drover. 18 cm long.

£25 — £40

575 A farmer's gig, cat. no. 20F, complete with seated farmer. The horse is not original but from the type used on the farm cart cat. no. 40F. The original horse can be seen just in front of fence, in the next illustration.

*£30 — £50 (original gig)*

576 A selection of Britains Home Farm items.

*£1 — £3 (animals)*
*50p — £1 (fencing)*
*50p — £1 (trees)*
*£1.50 — £3 (figures)*

577 A Britains Fordson Major tractor, cat. no. 128F, finished in the authentic Fordson colours of dark blue with orange wheels. Shown here complete with driver. This is an early post-war model with narrow front tyres and tapered steering column, attached to disc harrow, cat. no. 135F and roller, cat. no. 136F. Also shown is a four farrow plough, cat. no. 138F.

*£75 — £100 (tractor)*
*£8 — £12 (harrow)*
*£6 — £10 (roller)*
*£8 — £12 (plough)*

578 Two accessories for the Britains Model Farm are no. 130F the farm trailer, and no. 129F the timber trailer. These items were intended to be towed behind no. 127F or no. 128F Fordson tractors. Various colours available. Circa 1950.

*£8 — £12 (trailer)*
*£15 — £20 (timber trailer)*

579 From Britains Zoological Series, a selection of pieces available, including no. 922 Ostrich, no. 919 Coconut Palm, no. 954 Gorilla with pole, no. 937 giant tortoise.

*£1 — £2 (each)*

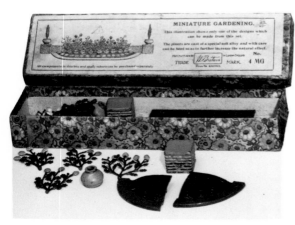

580 Catalogue no. 4MG (Miniature Gardening) by Britains. Various permutations are suggested, and the label design shows an attractive formal setting. It is interesting to note the manufacturer's comment that the plants ''with care can be bent so as to further increase the natural effect.''

*£15 — £20 (with original box)*

581 A circular border, together with a variety of plants. Britains. Circa 1935.

*£10 — £15 (with original box)*

582 Left: No doubt the permutations of some model gardens were infinite; shown here is a square border, no. 3MG, with individual plants to arrange. Britains also made available components in transparent paper bags. Pre-war. Top Right: Complete Britains greenhouses are scarce. A complete model should consist of four side panels, roof, door and runner boards, cat. no. 053. Also shown is a Britains cold frame. 1930s. Centre: For the complete garden, a summerhouse, decorative and functional. The base is of card construction. Circa 1935. Lower Right: Made by Taylor and Barrett, this costermonger's donkey cart comes complete with bananas and baskets of vegetables. Note from the manufacturer's label: "vegetables and baskets can be bought separately." These items are now becoming fairly scarce. 1930s.

|  |  |
|---|---|
| *£10 — £15 (3MG with original box)* | *£5 — £8 (summerhouse)* |
| *£35 — £50 (greenhouse)* | *£20 — £30 (donkey cart)* |
| *£60 — £80 (greenhouse with original box)* | *£40 — £50 (donkey cart with original box)* |

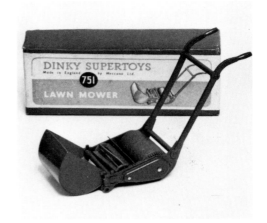

583 Again by Taylor and Barrett, this coster's set lacks the coster shown on box label. Circa 1930s.

*£25 — £40 (complete)*

584 Totally out of scale compared to other models in the Dinky range, this Supertoys lawn mower has rotating cutter and detachable grass box. Numbered 751 and illustrated in a 1952 catalogue and priced 6s.10d, (34p). By 1959 this number was used for a police hut.

*£20 — £30*

585 A pair of brass-barrelled model cannons 9.5 cm long, the barrels impressed with Marklin trade mark. Circa 1900.

*£15 — £25*

586 A well-made Marklin gun (probably an anti-aircraft piece) with working breech and facilities for adjusting elevation and windage. Finished in grey with black details. Circa 1912. 13 cm high.

*£80 — £120*

587 An attractively boxed set of traditional wooden toy soldiers (3.5 cm high) together with a wooden fort with drawbridge, sentry boxes, trees and two-horse gun teams.

*£40 — £50 (set)*

588 A good early 20th century sectional wooden toy fort with heavily textured surfaces having turreted towers, gateways, chapel. When not in use, the shaped base can be utilised as a storage box. 54 cm wide, 36.5 cm deep.

*£30 — £50*

589 Probably from the immediate post-war period, this sectional painted wooden toy fort incorporates half timber fronted buildings, towers, traditional drawbridge.

*£18 — £25*

# Pedal Power

Shortly after the introduction of the horseless carriage, children's pedal powered cars were being produced. By 1910 quite elaborate models were available with oil lamps, pneumatic tyres, leather upholstery, horns, glass windscreens and hoods. These were generally chain driven, cycle fashion, utilising only one rear wheel. Early models were coach built in timber and sheet metal and produced in very limited quantities. These are therefore very rare.

After World War I toy manufacturers introduced crank back axles with pedal activated connecting rods and more sheet metal was included in the body, the all metal construction car appearing in the 1930s. Many models from this period were produced by Lines Brothers and, depending upon their price, were either imitation production cars or crude representations. Some of these models will have battery operated lights, fake plugs and suspension details, opening boots, etc.

After World War II the quality of the pedal car standardised at a lower level except for those produced by disabled Welsh miners for Austin Motors.

Remember that many pedal cars have disappeared or are found in a dilapidated state owing to the fact that they were so large they were often relegated to the garden. These can be an interesting restoration project for the competent amateur.

*Value Point*
Originality of fitting, tyres, etc. + + +

*Colour Plate 41. Vauxhall pedal car, c.1932. (See also 603, page 203.)*

# CHILDREN'S TOY MOTOR CARS, ROCKING HORSES, Etc.

**The Landau Automobile** No. 526.

This is a good size Car. Superior quality Coachwork Body, with Side Wings and Step (covered Rubber); 9/16 Wired-on Tyred Wheels with Malleable Hubs. Back and sides nicely upholstered in art colours, white, or to order. Upholstered throughout and Adjustable Seat. Ratchet Starting Handle. Two Nickel-plated Lamps; superior Hooter. Coach painted in White, Crimson, Navy, or Dark Green, or to order. Price .. .. **92 6**

Quotations given for Special Shape Motor Cars on receipt of customers' requirements. A good margin of time is required for Special Designs.

Model Limousines, Landaulettes, Four-Seat and Two-Seat Touring Cars, Glass Wind Screens, Electric Lights, Motor Cars for Roundabouts, etc., quoted for.

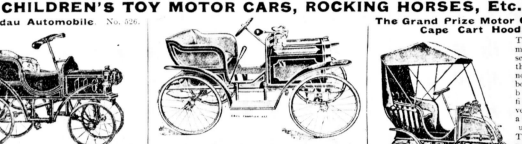

Ball Bearings Throughout.
**The Featherweight Champion Motor-Car**
No. 457). **Registered Design.**
This Motor is the last word in luxury, easy working, light weight and finish.
25½ in. gear, very easy working. Ball-bearing wheels, pedals and chain bracket. Long, easy riding steel springs. Parallel wheel steering by our own registered movement. Cycle quality chainwork with ½ in. pitch roller chain. Weldless steel cycle tubing. Tangent spoke wire wheels with ¾ in. wired-on rubber tyres, or with artillery pattern wood wheels, with wired-on rubber tyres. Powerful metal brake acting on both wheels, with automatic spring clutch. Starting handle with ratchet action. Two head-lights and two number-boards. Good quality motor horn. Finely proportioned body to scale with wide mudguards and steps. Tool box, with spanner. Aluminium steering wheel. Body upholstered in motor style in fine quality material.
This motor is far and away the lightest of its size on the market. No effort is needed to propel it. Position of seat and pedals can be adjusted. Suitable for boy or girl 7 to 14 years of age. Nickel-plated fittings throughout. If for a girl, a gear case can be fitted (Extra). Cape cart hood can be fitted extra (see below). Length over all, 51 in. Width over all, 25 in. Height over all, 26½ in.
Price as illustrated, with ¾ in. wired-on tyre .. .. .. **£7 2 6**
Cape Cart Hood in brown cloth on brass frame to order 10/- extra.
Glass Wind Screen, framed wood to order, £1 extra.
With 4 Dunlop pneumatic tyred wheels, £3 19 6 extra.
(These reduce weight about 5 lb.

**The Grand Prize Motor Car with Cape Cart Hood.**

This Automobile deserves more than ordinary notice. The body is coach-built and finished in very best style and finely upholstered. The side panels are curvated and not flat. It is the last word in graceful and refined construction. The price in comparison with the excellent quality given is extremely moderate.
Price, finished in Coach Blue or Dark Green, **72/-**
Starting Handle with Rachet arrangement 1 6 extra.

590 Of the highest quality and with a real attempt to imitate the automobiles of the period, these pedal cars from Gamages 1911 catalogue incorporated the best refinements and materials. A glance at the specification of the 'Featherweight Champion' with its sprung suspension, coach lined body and working oil lamps, etc., confirms this. With full specification this model cost 12 gns. From the same catalogue, one could have bought a 'gents cycle' for £3 19s. 9d!

*£300 — £500 (landau)*
*£800 — £1,200 (Featherweight Champion)*
*£300 — £500 (Grand Prize)*

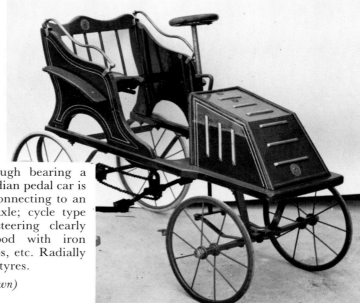

591 Of unknown origin, although bearing a 'Thistle' trade mark, this Edwardian pedal car is propelled by cycle type pedals connecting to an inch pitch chain driving rear axle; cycle type saddle; simple but effective steering clearly visible. Constructed from wood with iron fittings, brass handrails, hub caps, etc. Radially spoked wheels with solid rubber tyres.

*£300 — £400 (as shown)*

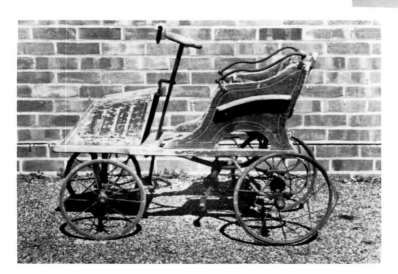

592 An illustration of the previous model in as found, unrestored condition. Note collapsed near side rear wheel; otherwise complete.

*£100 — £200 (as shown)*

593 An early front wheel drive tricycle of simple construction and radially spoked wheels. This type was produced from c.1910-30.

*£30 — £50*

594 An early example of a Lines Bros. Tri-ang pedal car. Unlike some of its predecessors, this model came complete and not in kit form. Note the tin body on wooden chassis, wood rimmed steering wheel, brass hub caps, rubber tyres. The trade mark is clearly visible on the radiator. Circa 1919. 91 cm long overall.

*£80 — £100*

**UNDERGEAR AND WHEELS FOR TOY MOTORS.**
Comprising ½″ cemented tyre wheels, 10″ × 10″, with ½″ spindles and chain wheels, 5-hole steering axle, pedal, bracket and chain.
No. 8097/1900 ... ... ... Retail Price **30/-** set.

**UNDERGEAR, WHEELS & STEERING FOR TOY MOTORS.**
Comprising ½″ cemented tyre wheels, 10 × 10″, with ½″ spindle and chain wheels, with patent steering axle, steering column and wheel, pedal, bracket and chain.
No. 8098/2500 ... ... ... Retail Price **37/6** set.

| | | PEDAL MOTOR PARTS. | Retail Price |
|---|---|---|---|
| No. 8151/608 | | Patent Front Axle for No. 8098 ... | **10/-** each |
| ,, | 8152/100 | Patent Front Axle for No. 8097 ... | **1/6** ,, |
| ,, | 8153/200 | Back Axle ... ... ... | **3/-** ,, |
| ,, | 8154/200 | Steering Column and Wheel ... | **3/-** ,, |
| ,, | 8155/504 | Bracket, complete with Chain Wheel, Cranks and Pedals ... | **8/-** set |
| ,, | 8156/100 | R.T. Pedals ... ... ... | **1/6** pair |

**UNDERGEAR COMPLETE. LESS WHEELS.**
Steering Column and Wheel, Bracket, Chain, Back Axle, etc., and Springs.
No. 8099/1800 ... ... ... Retail Price **27/-** set.

**SPECIAL SET FITTINGS.**
Comprising Speedometer, Clock, Licence Holder, and Clicking Starting Handle.
No. 8160/104 ... ... ... Retail Price **2/-** per set.

595 An attractive 1920s chain driven pedal car possibly constructed from a kit, with wooden chassis, metal bonnet, radiator, adjustable seat. It has a folding dicky seat, external hand brake, imitation gear change, wood rimmed steering wheel, starting handle. Originally finished in mid-blue.

*£300 — £500*

596 Included in the Manufacturers Accessories Co. Ltd. catalogue of the 1923-24 season was this do-it-yourself pedal car kit. At this time most pedal cars were chain driven and it was left to father to produce the body to go with the provided undergear; some interesting designs may therefore be encountered.

597 Known as an 'Empire Racer' in a 1924 catalogue, this simply constructed cart was steered by a child's feet and propelled by push-pull action on the thrust bar. Effective speedwise, but out of favour in the 1930s.

*£50 — £90*

# TOY MOTORS

## STRONG ATTRACTIVE TOYS.

Body 34 in. Crank drive, fitted with Balloon Discs, Mudguards, Windscreen, Horn, Petrol Can, Mirror and imitation Lamps.
**X 1200 2806** - - - - - **each 39/6**
Colour: Powder Blue.

Very well made and finished. Crank Drive. The back axle is sprung on coil springs. Measures 34 in. × 14 in. Fitted with Balloon Discs, Mudguards, Horn, Side Lamps, Petrol Can and Mirror.
**X 1202 3906** - - - - **each 55/-**
Colours: Powder Blue and Red.

Strong Toy, double crank drive. Body 29 in. Seat 12 in. wide. Fitted with 8 × ½ in. Disc Wheels. Rubber tyred. Wired-on tyres.
**X 1206 1600** - - - - **each 22/6**
Painted Red.

Body 38 in., upholstered Seat and Back. Dummy Hood. Horn, Head, Side and Rear Lamps, Licence, Mirror, Petrol Can, Tool Box, Luggage Carrier. Nickel-plated Radiator and Buffer Bar, 1⅜ in. Tyres. Aluminium Disc Wheels. **Chain Drive.**
**X 1204 8906** - - - - - **each £6 5 0**
Painted Royal Blue and Fawn, two-colour effect.

Body 42 in. Crank Drive, fitted with Balloon Disc Wheels, Horn and Windscreen.
**X 1208 2406** - - - - **each 35/-**
Colours: Powder Blue, or Red.

**Chain Drive.** Very strongly made Body, measures 36 in. Upholstered Seat and Back. Fitted with Door, N.P. Windscreen, Head and Side Lamps, Petrol Can, Luggage Grid, Clock, Speeds, Dummy Hood, Horn, etc. 10 in. Balloon Disc Wheels.
**X 1210 5906** - - - - - **each 80/-**
Colours: Maroon and Grey, two-colour effect.

**29-33, GT. EASTERN ST., LONDON, E.C.2.**

598 The 1929 East London Rubber Co. autumn catalogue illustrated these pedal cars which they retailed. Note the luxurious model, lower left, based on a Rolls Royce.

| | | |
|---|---|---|
| *£40 — £60 (top left)* | *£50 — £80 (top centre)* | *£20 — £40 (top right)* |
| *£150 — £250 (below left)* | *£60 — £80 (below centre)* | *£125 — £175 (below right)* |

# TOY MOTORS

## TANSADS MOTORS

### " WIZARD "

A modern super Sports Car. A real motor car in miniature, with beautiful lines and a shaped panelled back with luxuriously upholstered bucket seat and back. Adjustable windscreen, streamline mudguards, instrument board. Full accessories include : horn, two plated streamline lamps, chromium-plated bumper, direction indicator and bonnet ornaments. 11 × 1¼ in. moulded tyres on tangent spoke wheels. Ball-bearing back axle on coil springs. Colours : Red, Blue or Green. Length 50 in., width 22½ in., height 21 in.

X 1300/5108 - - - - - - - each 77/6

### " TEN-FOUR "

A high-class all-metal Car, with door and luxuriously upholstered bucket seat, highly finished sloping radiator, chromium-plated bumper. Pressed streamline guards and 9-in. **easy-clean** wheels are fitted. Streamline plated lamps and chromium-plated ornaments on bonnet. Windscreen, horn, petrol-can, oil-can and direction indicator. Ball-bearing back axle. Length 43½ in., width 19 in., height 18½ in. Colours : Red, Blue, Pale Green.

X 1301/3804 - - - - - - each 57/6

### " HORNET " RACER

This model has been completely re-designed, with a metal panelled body, upholstered back rest and streamline guards. Special features are chromium-plated front bumper bar, **easy-clean** wheels, folding windscreen, 9-in. diameter plated streamline lamps, direction indicator and bonnet ornaments. Ball-bearing back axle. Colours : Red, Blue, Pale Green. Length 44 in., width 19 in., height 19 in.

X 1302/3300 - - - - - - - each 49/6

### " BROOKLANDS "

A new sports model with streamline front and tapered tail. Attractive radiator and bumper bar, adjustable bucket seat with back rest, 7-in. steering wheel, instrument board, two plated streamline lamps, windscreen, horn, and direction indicator, 9½-in., **easy-clean** wheels and mudguards, as illustrated. A very serviceable and attractive model of latest design and attractive appearance. Ball-bearing back axle. Colours : Red, Blue or Green. Length 45 in., width 19 in., height 18 in.

X 1303/2804 - - - - - - each 42/6

599 Ten years later, the East London Rubber Co. offered this range in their catalogue. Note the utilitarian appearance and competitive prices aimed now at a wider market.

£100 — £150 (Wizard)
£80 — £120 (Ten-Four and Hornet Racer)
£60 — £80 (Brooklands)

600 This French produced 'Eureka' Bugatti pedal car is modelled on the type 35, and is entirely of pressed steel construction having free-wheel incorporated in drive. It was originally fitted with electric lights and wings (missing on model shown). A spare wheel was also carried. Circa 1930. Approx 6ft. long.

*£500 — £800*

601 A Lines Bros. version of a 1930s Rolls Royce, this model has tubular steel chassis with cantilever leaf spring suspension, wooden body with opening steel bonnet, dicky seat, rear-mounted spare wheel, opening door with cast step bearing trade mark, and double bumper blades.

*£225 — £350*

602 Another Lines Bros. Rolls Royce, this time their much sought after electric powered version. It is similar in detail to the previous model but has a longer wheelbase chassis with extended bonnet, electric lights, etc. This model was advertised in September 1933 at the then expensive price of 30 guineas and the specification quoted "length 6 feet, height 28½", width 28"; driving unit 12 volt Lucas powerful electric motor mounted on rear axle; lighting equipment Lucas 5 lamps with 12 volt bulbs (direction indicators are 2 volt only); batteries two 6 volt Lucas car-type; 5 wheels including spare, ballbearing hubs and chromium plated rims, Dunlop 2¼" pneumatic tyres, brake, band type operating on rear axle". A very fortunate child — clearly expressed by the grin!

*£800 — £1,200*

603 Again by Lines Bros., this Vauxhall pedal car, c.1932, conveys the stylish lines of cars of the period. Well constructed, it has a wooden chassis and part body, bonnet of steel with louvres and typical Vauxhall flutes, fold flat windscreen, opening luggage compartment, spare petrol and oil cans, horn and electric lights. Suspension is of leaf spring type with shackles, pneumatic tyres, bumper bars. Available in various colours. This model represents the more expensive and desirable 1930s' product. 145 cm long. (See also Colour Plate 41, page 196.)

*£750 — £1,000*

604 From *The Meccano Magazine*, December 1933, a selection of Tri-ang pedal cars available at a wide range of prices from the simply constructed 'Comet' to the sophisticated 'Magna'.

*£20 — £40 (Comet)*
*£200 — £300 (Magna Racer and Magna No. 8)*
*£80 — £120 (Bentley)*
*£100 — £150 (Wasp)*

605 This Lines Bros. Daimler sports pedal car has a wooden body and chassis, cycle type mudguards, front turn with steering, bumper bars, coil sprung rear suspension. It is fitted with pneumatic tyres, 12½ ins. x 2¼ ins., which are still available at the present time, but the model was also produced with solid rubber tyres. In 1939 this model was advertised in the Brown Bros. catalogue at £5, or £7 4s.9d. (£7 23½ p) with pneumatic tyres. Circa 1938. 136 cm long.

*£150 — £300*

606 Again from the Lines Bros. extensive pedal car range, a Triumph Dolomite sports car. The model seen here is a restored example with wooden body and chassis, pneumatic tyres, spare wheel, imitation head-lamps, etc. Circa 1938.

*£120 — £200*

## TOY MOTORS—continued
### "RAMBLER" SERIES

Pressed Steel Latest Type Streamline Body, Side Door, Airflow Radiator with Mascot, 9″ Balloon Disc Wheels, ⅞″ Rubber Tyres, Magna Hub Caps, Ball Bearing Back Axle, Front and Rear Pressed Steel Bumpers, Adjustable Windscreen, Number Plate, Head and Side Lamps, Streamline Mudguards, Adjustable Upholstered Seat, Hand Brake, Dummy Hood, Petrol and Oil Cans.
For ages 5 to 7 years.  Length 45″.  Crank Drive.
No. 27/140cs/4109 .. .. .. .. .. each £3 2 9

Aluminium Streamline Body, Side Door, Latest Type Radiator, 8½″ Tangent-spoked Wheels with Magna Hubs, 1½″ Jointless Sponge Rubber Tyres, Front and Rear Pressed Steel Bumpers, Adjustable Windscreen, Number Plate, Electric Side Lamps, Dome Steel Mudguards, Dummy Hood, Luggage Locker, Chromium Plated Fittings, Petrol and Oil Cans.
For ages 4 to 6 years.  Length 41″.  Crank Drive.
No. 27/140e/5208 .. .. .. .. .. each £3 19 0

Pressed Steel Body, Tubular Chassis with Sprung Rear Axle, Side Door, Streamline Radiator, 8½″ Tangent-spoked Wheels, 10″ × 1½″ Jointless Sponge Rubber Tyres, Magna Hubs, Ball Bearing Back Axle, Front and Rear Tubular Bumpers, Adjustable Windscreen, Number Plate, Dummy Head Lamps, Electric Side Lamps, Stop and Go Sign and Electric Horn, Streamline Mudguards, Adjustable Upholstered Seat, Dummy Hood, Petrol and Oil Cans, Chromium Plated Wheels.
For ages 5 to 7 years  Length 45″.  Crank and Chain Drive.
No. 27/140g/7506 .. .. .. .. .. each £5 13 3

Pressed Steel, Latest Type Streamline Body, Tubular Chassis, Side Door, Airflow Radiator, 8½″ Tangent-spoked Wheels, 10″ × 1½″ Jointless Sponge Rubber Tyres, Magna Hubs, Ball Bearing Back Axle, Front and Rear Pressed Steel Bumpers, Adjustable Windscreen, Number Plate, Electric Head Lamps, Stop and Go Sign and Electric Horn, Streamline Mudguards, Adjustable Upholstered Seat, Dummy Hood, Petrol and Oil Cans, Chromium Plated Wheels.
For ages 5 to 7 years.  Length 45″.  Crank and Chain Drive.
No. 27/140h/7703 .. .. .. .. .. each £5 16 0

Wooden Body, Side Door, Daimler type Radiator with Mascot and Plated Rim, 11″ Tangent-spoked Wheels, 13″ × 1½″ Jointless Sponge Rubber Tyres, Magna Hubs, Ball Bearing Back Axle. Two sets of Pedals, Front Axle mounted on Springs, Front and Rear Pressed Steel Bumpers, Adjustable Windscreen, Dummy Hood, Head and Side Lamps, Klakker Horn, Hand Brake, Racing Mudguards, Upholstered Seat and Back-rest:  Petrol and Oil Cans, Nickel Plated Fittings.
For ages 4 to 8 years.  Length 53½″.  Crank Drive.
No. 27/140n/6608 .. .. .. .. each £5 0 0
Ditto with 12½″ × 2½″ Dunlop Balloon Tyred Wheels, Chromium Plated Fittings.
No. 27/140np 9606 .. .. .. .. each £7 4 9

Wooden Body, Tubular Chassis and Sprung Axles, Side Door, Vauxhall Type Radiator, 11″ Tangent-spoked Wheels 13″ × 1½″ Jointless Sponge Rubber Tyres, Magna Hubs, Ball Bearing Back Axle.  Two sets of Pedals, Front and Rear Pressed Steel Bumpers, Adjustable Windscreen, Head and Side Lamps, Racing Mudguards, Upholstered Adjustable Seat and Back-rest, Luggage Locker, Dummy Hood, Petrol and Oil Cans, Nickel Plated Fittings.
For ages 4 to 8 years.  Length 52″.  Crank Drive.
No. 27/140to/7309 .. .. .. .. .. each £5 11 0
Ditto with 12½″ × 2½″ Dunlop Balloon Tyred Wheels.  Chromium Plated Fittings.
No. 27/140tp/10809 .. .. .. .. each £8 3 3

607  From the 1939 Brown Brothers general catalogue, a selection of Tri-ang pedal cars illustrating the relatively high expense of such playthings. Note the difference the Dunlop balloon tyres and chromium-plated fittings made to the original prices, and the typical pre-war necessity for having petrol and oil cans as part of the specification.

*£75 — £100 (top left)*      *£75 — £100 (top right)*
*£100 — £150 (centre left)*      *£100 — £150 (centre right)*
*£150 — £300 (below left)*      *£200 — £400 (below right)*

608 This immediate post-war pedal racing car was normally retailed in bright red paintwork. Of simple pressed steel construction with imitation balloon tyres using thin rubber to periphery of wheel. Note the external exhaust pipe with Brooklands fishtail. Circa 1946-50. 120 cm overall.

*£50 — £70*

609 A cheaply made pedal car in the style of a Ford Zephyr having dummy steering column, gear change, bulb horn, bumper bar, windscreen and pressed balloon type wheels and tyres. Circa 1950s. 100 cm long.

*£40 — £60*

610 An Austin J40 roadster pedal car produced by Austin from 1949 to 1971. These models were produced by disabled miners in South Wales, and their specification included: adjustable treadle drive, handbrake, roller bearing hubs, detachable pressed steel wheels with Dunlop 12½ ins. x 2¼ ins. tyres, pressed steel bodywork, felt padded seating and leather cloth upholstery, dummy O.H.V. 'engine' complete with sparking plugs and leads, battery operated headlamps and horn, chrome trim. 160 cm long, 69 cm wide, 56 cm high, 43 kilograms. Available in standard Austin colours, approximately 32,000 were produced. Although the model was labelled 'Junior', in catalogues these models were known as 'Joy Cars' by the Austin factory.

*£150 — £200 (as shown, in excellent condition with original transfer)*

611 A playworn example of the J40 roadster. Many will have deteriorated and have been scrapped as this large model was frequently left out in the garden. 'Flying A' bonnet motif was deleted from the design on later models as mascots on real cars fell from favour for safety reasons.

*£80 — £100 (as shown)*

# Toy Grading Terms

Collectors will be familiar with the word 'mint'. The following are suggestions for other grading terms.

**Factory Fresh**   Mint condition, as made, no damage to product, though packaging may have suffered slightly.

**Sunday**   Complete and showing signs of only minimum damage, minor paint loss, slight scuffs, etc. As though played with only on a Sunday and under the supervision of an adult.

**Enjoyed**   Evidence of wear, some paint loss or deterioration, minor attached accessories missing: lamps, buffers, bumpers, etc. Still generally acceptable. As though played with considerably, but not to the extent of contempt.

**Playworn**   Considerable evidence of use, dents, paint damage, rust, incomplete. Worth collecting only if scarce or as a temporary 'space filler' and purchased at a reasonable price.

(These gradings can be expanded by adverbs such as almost, nearly, about, etc.)

# Historical Events

| | |
|---|---|
| 1851 | The Great Exhibition, London |
| 1864 | George Pullman builds the first sleeping car for railroad use |
| 1886 | Daimler's first successful automobile |
| 1898 | Airship experiments in Italy and Germany |
| 1900 | Boxer Rebellion in China |
| 1901 | Ballooning altitude record of 35,000 feet |
| 1903 | Wilbur and Orville Wright make pioneering flight |
| 1906 | First practical Zeppelin airship |
| 1909 | Henry Ford begins mass production of Model T |
| | Blériot flies monoplane from Calais to Dover |
| 1911 | Amundsen discovers the South Pole |
| 1914 | Start of World War I |
| 1918 | End of World War I |
| 1921 | Great Britain Railway Act leading to the formation of four main line railways: L.M.S.R., L.N.E.R., G.W.R. and S.R. |
| 1927 | Lindbergh makes the first continuous transatlantic flight |
| 1928 | Walt Disney introduces Mickey Mouse |
| 1929 | Segrave smashes the land speed record in Golden Arrow |
| 1939 | Start of World War II |
| 1945 | End of World War II |
| 1948 | British Railways passes into public ownership |

# Materials and Compositions

encountered in the manufacture of toys

Wood
Iron
Brass
Lead
Tin
Chrome plating
Nickel plating

Composition
Glass
Bakelite
Plastic
Perspex
Rubber

# Prices Comparison 1970-1980

|  | 1970 | 1980 |
|---|---|---|
| Early Trains: Bing gauge I clockwork | £10 | £150 |
| Later Trains: King George V gauge 0 | £8 | £85 |
| Rolling Stock: Bogie coach | £3 | £20 |
| Stationary Steam: Bing middle range | £7 | £75 |
| Early Novelty: Lehmann mule | £10 | £100 |
| Later Novelty: Mickey Mouse organ grinder | £15 | £600 |
| Early Road Transport: Bing limousine | £500 | £1,000 |
| Later Road Transport: P2 Alfa Romeo, boxed | £40 | £600 |
| Die-cast Transport: Dinky 36 series car | £2 | £15 |
| Die-cast Miscellaneous: Box of Highlanders | £5 | £30 |
| Pedal Power: Austin J40, new | £30 | £150 |

# Patent Abbreviations

| | |
|---|---|
| Breveté S.G.D.G. | French patent |
| D.R.G.M. | German utility patent |
| D.R.P. | German full patent applying |
| ENG. | England (on patents) |
| Ges. Gesch. | German indication of some patent applying on part or whole |
| U.S.P. | United States patent |
| U.S. Zone Germany, made in | German manufacture, c.1945-50 |
| Western Germany, made in | German manufacture, c.1948 onwards |

# Toy Manufacturers and Trade Marks

The list below is by no means comprehensive but is intended as a preliminary guide only. Many of the initials can be found in various formations. It may be noted that the letter N when used as the last letter usually indicates Nuremburg as the place of manufacture.

| Name | Country of origin | Trade name and trade marks | Name | Country of origin | Trade name and trade marks |
|------|-------------------|----------------------------|------|-------------------|----------------------------|
| Adam | Germany | Girl standing on globe motif | Kienberger | Germany | Huki |
| | | | Kindler & Briel | Germany | Kibri |
| Alps | Japan | Alps | Kinsbury | U.S.A. | Kinsbury |
| Ammon | Germany | C.A. | Köhler | Germany | GKN |
| Arnold | Germany | A. Arnold | Kraus | Germany | JKCO Fandor |
| Bassett-Lowke | England | Lowko | Krauss | Germany | WK |
| Biller | Germany | Key with B motif | Lehmann | Germany | EPL, ⊑ |
| Bing | Germany | G.B.N., B.W. | Levy | Germany | Gely |
| Blomer & Schüler | Germany | B&S 'Jumbo' | Lineol | Germany | Three ducks motif, Lineol |
| Bonnet | France | Vébé | | | |
| Brimtoy | England | Brimtoy | Lines Brothers | England | Tri-ang, Minic |
| Britain | England | Britains Proprietors | Lionel | U.S.A. | Lionel |
| | | | Mangold | Germany | Gama |
| Bub | Germany | KBN, KB, BUB | Markes | Germany | Dux |
| Burnett | England | St. George motif | Märklin | Germany | GM & Cie |
| Cardini | Italy | Cardini | Martin | France | F.M. |
| Carette | Germany | G.C.C.N, G.C. & C. | Marx | U.S.A. | Marlines |
| | | | Meccano Ltd. | England | Meccano |
| Chad Valley | England | Chad Valley, Ubilda | Meier | Germany | Dog and cart motif |
| Citroën | France | Citroën | Meteor | Holland | Meteor |
| Compagnie Industrielle du Jouet | France | CIJ | Mettoy | England | Mettoy, Corgi |
| | | | Moschkowitz | Germany | MMN |
| Crescent Toy Company | England/ Wales | New Moon motif | Neuhierl | Germany | JNF |
| | | | Nomura | Japan | T.N. |
| Distler | Germany | Thistle or Globe motif | Oro-Werke | Germany | Orobr |
| | | | Payà | Spain | Paya, RAI |
| Doll | Germany | D.C. | Plank | Germany | EP and Wings motif |
| Eberl | Germany | H.E.N. | | | |
| Einfalt | Germany | GEN, Technofix | Radiquet & Massiot | France | |
| Faivre | France | F.V. | Rico | Spain | RSA |
| Falk | Germany | J.F. | Rissmann | Germany | WR |
| Fischer, G. | Germany | G.F. | Roitel | France | C.R. |
| Fischer, H. | Germany | Fish motif | Rossignol | France | C.R. |
| Fleischmann | Germany | G.F.N. | Schmid | Germany | Gescha |
| Greppert & Kelch | Germany | G & K | Schönner | Germany | J.S. |
| Günthermann | Germany | SG | Schreyer & Co. | Germany | Schuco |
| Gutmann | France | Memo | Schrödel | Germany | Ideal |
| Hafner | U.S.A. | New York Flyer | Schuhmann | Germany | A.S. |
| Hausser | Germany | Elastolin | Seidel | Germany | MS |
| Heller and Schiller | Germany | Husch | Staudt | Germany | Schloss motif and ST |
| Hess | Germany | JLH, Hessmobil | | | |
| Hill | England | Johillco | Stock & Co. | Germany | Stock |
| Höfler | Germany | JH | Structo | U.S.A. | Structo |
| Hornby | England | Meccano | Sutcliffe | England | Sutcliffe |
| I.N.G.A.P. | Italy | INGAP | Taylor & Barratt | England | T & B |
| Issmayer | Germany | JAJ | Tipp | Germany | Tippco, TCo |
| Ives | U.S.A. | I.M.C. | Trix | Germany | Trix |
| Jouef | France | Jouef | V.E.B. | Germany | VEB |
| Jouets de Paris | France | JEP | Wells | England | Wells |
| Joustra | France | Joustra | Whiteley Tansley & Co. | England | Whitanco |
| Keim | Germany | K. Keim | | | |
| Kellermann | Germany | C.KO | Wimmer | Germany | HWN |

# Trade Terminology

A light-hearted look at some of the terms used by dealers.

**As bought**
As purchased — a phrase used to exonerate the vendor of any moral or legal responsibility with regard to the item he is selling (e.g. 'What is it?' 'Not sure, sir, but it's as bought.') Much used by Irish knockers. Auctioneers use similar terms, 'As found' or 'With all faults'.

**Bought in**
An item unsold at auction, where the price has failed to reach the reserve. Such an item might appear to have been sold, but has failed to reach its reserve and has therefore been 'bought back' by the auctioneer acting on behalf of the vendor.

**Collector's piece**
Originally a term to describe a fine piece that only a connoisseur would appreciate; often now debased to the sort of thing that only an eccentric enthusiast on the subject would want; normally overpriced, and often totally undesirable.

**Commercial**
1. Not necessarily a fine or completely original piece, but readily saleable. 2. The description of a dealer's goods as 'commercial' is not a term of approbation and is often used by a specialist or another dealer who is more financially successful.

**Estimate**
The price suggested by the auctioneer as the amount a lot is likely to fetch. Usually a tortuous compromise between the need to prove to the vendor the auctioneer's competence as a valuer and an effort to persuade as many potential buyers as possible to attend.

**Flea market**
A collection of stalls where the variety of pieces sold is very considerable, often rubbish, and usually overpriced. Prices asked are normally subject to negotiation.

**Fresh**
Unseen by dealers in the locality.

**Hammer price**
The auction price.

**Honest**
A piece which is 'right', but simple in construction or decoration.

**In the book**
An attempt to establish an immediate provenance for an item otherwise hard to compliment by reference to standard works, or indeed any printed source. An attempt to confer immediate acceptance and respectability.

**Investment item**
Used descriptively by a dealer of something for which he has paid too much.

**Knocker**
One who calls on a private house uninvited and tries to buy goods, usually below current market value.

**Knocking down**
At auction, the selling of an item.

**Knocking out**
The selling of goods at very small profit, very quickly, with the object of (a) bringing in money quickly or (b) disposing of an item for which one has paid too much.

**Looker**
A serious buyer without the funds to acquire any goods.

**Old friends**
Items of whose company one has tired, which reappear regularly at auction, or those in a shop that have hitherto failed to find a buyer.

**Right**
An item which proves, on examination, to be of the period which at first sight it seemed to be, and in most important respects is original. Frequently used by antique dealers. (See 'Wrong'.)

**Ring**
A group of dealers who agree not to increase the price at auction by nominating one of their number to bid. An item so bought is re-auctioned privately afterwards and the difference in value split as agreed between the participants. There may be several opposing rings at one auction. (Illegal under the Auctions (Bidding Agreements) Act 1969.)

**Rooms, The**
The large auction houses, especially in London. Often used pretentiously in the provinces by those who would like their intimate familiarity with the London auction houses to be assumed.

**Runner**
One who makes his living by transporting pieces between dealers with a view to making a margin from the prospective sales, usually selling from his vehicle.

**Sleeper**
A piece which has been untouched for many years and is therefore more desirable than something recently restored.

**Speculative**
May or may not have considerable value, normally the latter.

**Stolen**
1. Goods illegally obtained as generally understood. 2. A very cheap purchase (see 'Touch').

**Touch**
A cheap item with a good profit ('a useful touch': an even better profit might be envisaged).

**Trade, The**
Antique dealers collectively.

**Trade price**
Cost of an item to a dealer, usually less than the marked ticket price (e.g. 'What's the trade on. . .?').

**Trotting**
1. At auction, the artificial increase in bidding with the intention of raising the selling price (running up). 2. Also used of runners (q.v.) taking their goods from place to place in the hope of finding a buyer.

**Unseen**
Bought without considered examination, often in the early hours with the aid of a torch.

**Wrong**
1. Faked, or so heavily adapted from what the item originally was that it now pretends to be what it is not. 2. An out-and-out fake. 3. An item that although possibly desirable has had a considerable amount of restoration, addition or alteration.

# Bibliography

*The Golden Age of Toys,* Jac Remise and Jean Fondin
*The Art of the Tin Toy,* David Pressland
*Mechanical Tin Toys in Colour,* Arno Weltens
*A Century of Model Trains,* Allen Levy
*Catalogue of Model Cars of the World,* J. Greilsamer and B. Azema
*The Encyclopedia of Toys,* Constance Eileen King
*The Great Toys of Georges Carette,* reprint of 1911 trade catalogue edited by
    Allen Levy
*Britain's Toy and Model Catalogue 1940,* reprint.
*History of the British Dinky Toy 1934-1964,* Cecil Gibson

In addition collectors are advised to seek out original manufacturers' catalogues where reprints are not available, though these will invariably be scarce.

**The following photographs are courtesy of Sotheby's Belgravia.**
**Colour Plates:** 2, 30.
**Black and White Plates:** 1-3, 5-13, 17, 18, 20-26, 31-37, 40-43, 45-47, 49-52, 54-68, 73, 74, 83-85, 87-90, 95-98, 103-105, 109, 122, 128, 131, 136-138, 149-160, 168-175, 182-184, 186, 189, 190, 194-204, 206-210, 213-217, 223, 224, 227-235, 238-240, 244, 246-248, 253, 257-260, 262-268, 270-276, 278-292, 295, 296, 299, 302-304, 306-316, 318, 319, 321, 323, 327-329, 331-333, 344-348, 351-357, 360-363, 369, 370, 377-379, 403, 405, 409-423, 425-431, 433, 435, 509, 529-531, 546, 548, 550-554, 556-560, 569.